ASHLEY MONTAGU

ON

# BEING
# HUMAN

Henry Schuman

NEW YORK

1951

To
Warder C. Allee and
Pitirim A. Sorokin
*Inspiring Students of Social Life*

" 'Men work together,' I told him from the heart,
Whether they work together or apart."

—Robert Frost

# Table of Contents

# Introduction

---

*T*O BE HUMAN IS TO BE IN DANGER. BY VIRTUE OF HIS possession of a unique nervous system, a nervous system which is much more plastic and educable than that of any other living animal, man is capable of confusing and endangering himself much more frequently. So-called civilized man of the Western world has befuddled and endangered himself to such a degree that he stands today on the very brink of destruction—self-destruction. The atom bomb, the hydrogen bomb, and bacteriological warfare are not the overpessimistic prognostications of dreary Jeremiahs; they are terrible realities. The first has already been used. The other two are ready for use. That anyone should be willing to employ such instruments of destruction at all is commentary enough upon the sorry pass to which man has come.

Such a pass that there are some who say that perhaps it would be just as well if Western man were to exterminate himself; it would certainly be one way in which to end all his problems. But suicide is never a solution to any human problem. It has often been said that the would-be suicide would never commit that final act of despair if he had a sympathetic ear into which to pour his troubles. What must be realized is that every human being is a problem in search of a solution. Some are merely parts of the problem, while others constitute part of the solution. Most of us—all of us—need a sympathetic ear and a solution to the problem which is the meaning of our lives— what our lives are, what they should be.

The problem of modern man is the problem of human relations—of man's relations to his fellow men and to himself. Personal, community, national, and international problems are first, fundamentally, and finally problems in human relations. This fact has been more or less vaguely recognized for a long time, and, indeed, conduct between persons as between nations has been, to some extent, conducted on the basis of certain theories of human relations —with the results that we all know. For example, the theory that war between nations is natural; that competition between men is necessary for their fullest development. Organized and secular religions, science, and philosophy have provided a style of life for human beings, but so far none of them have succeeded in solving the problem of how men can live in peace with their fellow men and with themselves. *And yet the knowledge to do just this is today available.*

It is the purpose of this little book to show that science is today in a position to teach man, in the most convincing of all manners, not only that his problems in human relations can be solved, but also the manner in which they must be solved.

During the last fifty years scientists have been conducting investigations on a wide variety of problems touching life. Many fundamental discoveries have been made, but, largely owing to the fact that we live in an age of over-specialization and compartmentalization of knowledge, no one has endeavored to put all this knowledge together and work out its meaning for the understanding of life and the nature of man. This task is not as herculean as may at first appear, for when I speak of putting "all this knowledge together," I mean all the relevant and significant knowledge sufficient to give sound answers to the questions asked. I have been at work on such a task for some years. Some of my findings have already become known and created considerable interest. I have been persuaded to produce them in this small book in the hope that they may reach as wide an audience as possible, several years before my larger and more technical book is likely to appear.

In sending this book out into the world, I should like to make it quite clear that, had it not been for the work of numerous other scientists, the present volume could never have been written. What I have done in this book is to integrate some of their more important findings and work out their significance for the understanding of life and the nature of man. There is, however, one original idea developed in this book, and it is fundamental. It constitutes my own contribution to the solution of an important problem. It will be properly underscored when I come to it.

The size of the book precludes the possibility of citing

more than the minimal fraction of the available facts necessary to prove the points which I attempt to establish in the present volume. I hope, however, that while the work is full of conclusions, it will not be received as a work full of purely declarative statements.

# 1

# What Is the Nature of Life?

# "The Survival of the Fittest"

ALL OF US ARE THE INHERITORS OF A TRADITION OF thought, relating to the nature of life, which has been handed down to us from the nineteenth century. Life, this view holds, is struggle, competition, the survival of the fittest. In the jungle, a fight with "Nature, red in tooth and claw," in society, the claw is perhaps gloved, and the fight is called a "struggle" in which "the race is to the swiftest," in which "the strongest survive and the weakest go to the wall."

It is commonly believed that much of the social thought of the nineteenth century was determined by the biological thought of the day. This belief is probably only partially true. It is, however, an open question whether it was not equally true that the social thought of the day determined the form of the biological thought.

The Industrial Revolution struck England first. Here was an hereditary aristocracy moving into business in a big way. Labor was cheap, and the employers saw to it that it was kept cheap as long as possible. The justification for employing small children and their parents in more or less continuous labor was that these were *inferior classes* of people who were valuable primarily as labor. There would always be poor people. Starvation was a law of nature.

The prejudices of a class have often been mistaken for the laws of nature, and during this early period of the Industrial Revolution, one great English social thinker, perhaps one of the leading social thinkers of any day, Thomas Robert Malthus (1766-1834) in fact attempted to prove in his *Essay on Population* that poverty and distress are unavoidable since population increases in geometric ratio while the means of subsistence increases in arithmetic ratio. As checks on population, Malthus at first accepted only war, famine, and disease, but later admitted that moral restraint might also act as a deterrent. This doctrine fitted the philosophy of the burgeoning industrial economy of England like a glove. It is perhaps not to be wondered at that in 1805 Malthus was made a professor at the College of the East India Company.

Human life consisted, according to Malthus, of a constant "struggle for existence" in which the weaker perpetually perished. It was the reading of this *Essay* in 1838 that gave Charles Darwin the clue to the basic principle of his theory expounded in *The Origin of Species by Means of Natural Selection, or the Preservation of Favored Races in the Struggle for Life*, which was published in November 1859. Throughout the rest of the nineteenth century, biologists were sedulously engaged in proving the Malthusian-Darwinian conception of the preservation of favored groups in the struggle for life.

What Darwin sought to do in *The Origin of Species*

may best be stated in his own words, which are here given from the first edition of his book.

> The Struggle for Existence amongst all organic beings throughout the world, which inevitably follows from their high geometrical powers of increase, will be treated of. This is the doctrine of Malthus, applied to the whole animal and vegetable kingdoms. As many more of each species are born than can possibly survive; and as, consequently, there is a frequently recurring struggle for existence, it follows that any being, if it vary however slightly in any manner profitable to itself, under the complex and sometimes varying conditions of life, will have a better chance of surviving, and thus be *naturally selected*. From the strong principle of inheritance, any selected variety will tend to propagate its new and modified form.

Malthus' book had been widely read, but Darwin's swept all before it. Not only did biologists now have a compass to steer by, but social philosophers and, particularly, enterprising industrialists and galloping imperialists, could now justify the exploitation of their workers, the maintenance of a permanent pool of unemployed labor, and the expropriation and exploitation of "inferior races." Biologists could claim that animals are in a constant state of "warfare" with one another, and that the two cardinal principles of natural selection are "the struggle for existence" and "the survival of the fittest." To cap it all, the poet Tennyson sang of "Nature, red in tooth and claw."

The law of life, according to such thinkers, is the law

of conflict. In his "Struggle For Existence" manifesto published in 1888, the distinguished scientist and excellent human being, Thomas Henry Huxley, wrote that "from the point of view of the moralist, the animal world is on about the same level as a gladiator's show. The creatures are fairly well treated, and set to fight; whereby the strongest, the swiftest and the cunningest live to fight another day. The spectator has no need to turn his thumb down, as no quarter is given." And again, with reference to primitive man, "the weakest and stupidest went to the wall, while the toughest and shrewdest, those who were best fitted to cope with their circumstances, but not the best in another way, survived. Life was a continuous free fight, and beyond the limited and temporary relations of the family, the Hobbesian war of each against all was the normal state of existence." [1]

To those who wished to have it otherwise, it was of no moment that Huxley, two years before his death, in the memorable Romanes Lecture which he delivered at Oxford in 1893, paused long enough to make his chief point, namely, that

> the influence of the cosmic process on the evolution of society is the greater the more rudimentary its civilization. Social checking means a checking of the cosmic process at every step and the substitution for it of another, which may be called the ethical process; the end of which is not the survival of those who may happen

[1] "The Struggle for Existence and Its Bearing Upon Man," *Nineteenth Century*, February 1888.

to be the fittest, in respect of the whole of the conditions which obtain, but of those who are ethically the best.

. . . the practice of that which is ethically the best— what we call goodness or virtue—involves a course of conduct which, in all respects, is opposed to that which leads to success in the cosmic struggle for existence. In place of ruthless self-assertion it demands self-restraint; in place of thrusting aside, or treading down, all competitors, it requires that the individual shall not merely respect, but shall help his fellows; its influence is directed, not so much to the survival of the fittest, as to the fitting of as many as possible to survive. It repudiates the gladiatorial theory of existence. . . .

It is from the neglect of these plain considerations that the fanatical individualism of our time attempts to apply the analogy of cosmic nature to society.[2]

But these final conclusions of Huxley came rather late in the day. His "Struggle for Existence" manifesto of five years earlier had summed up the more generally accepted viewpoint of his time.

That viewpoint, especially when taken out of context, gave a biological justification for competition between men of the same community, for competition—and conflict, war, between nations. It justified the exploitation of one's neighbors, one's competitors, and of inferior peoples by superior peoples, for does not nature give a biologically just decision?

[2] T. H. Huxley, *Evolution and Ethics*, the Romanes Lecture, Oxford University, 1893. Reprinted and quoted from T. H. Huxley and J. Huxley, *Touchstone For Ethics*, Harper & Bros., 1947, pp. 91-92.

Herbert Spencer, the English sociologist, was the leader in the application of such biologistic thought to human social behavior. He had early developed such ideas under the stimulus of Malthus and, with the advent of Darwinism, elaborated these ideas into a viewpoint which has come to be known as Social Darwinism. Social Darwinism defines the system of beliefs which has it that the same principles apply in the evolution and development of social as of biological life. Hence a nation's fitness to survive may be measured by war, that supreme agent of the evolutionary process, as General von Bernhardi and many other generals, and, more recently, Lord Elton, have held. Hence, too, as the late John D. Rockefeller (who certainly should have known) said, "The growth of a large business is merely a survival of the fittest."

By those who misused it, Darwinism was offered as no mere apology. It was more positive than that, it was a validation, a biological justification for competition. This doctrine has become part of the behavioral equipment, the system of overt beliefs of almost everyone in the Western world today. And so in the Middletowns of today we find it expressed, as it was to Helen and Robert Lynd in the words of a typical businessman, "You can't make the world all planned and soft. The strongest and best survive—that's the law of nature after all—always has been and always will be."

And this is modern man's conception of life: each for himself, and, if necessary, against his fellows. In America, indeed, this principle has become enshrined in the idea of "rugged individualism." In other lands of the Western world, it is perhaps not so clearly defined in a phrase, though as a reality it is well enough established. And so, in the Western world, each man has come to stand alone, "an island entire of itself" for if one is not for himself, who will be? Competition is the law of life—have not the scientists demonstrated it? So we compete.

Such is the law of life.

*This view of life is completely false.* Yet it largely motivates the conduct of most persons in the Western world. And it has brought man into the sorry state of personal, interpersonal, and international conflict in which he finds himself today.

The facts of biology, indeed, do provide a basis for human conduct, but those facts, as we know them today, point in a very different direction from that which the so-called Darwinians indicated. Their importance cannot be overemphasized. And it needs to be underscored here that Darwin himself was among the first to recognize their importance and to endeavor to make them known. Whether or not Darwin was outraged by the excesses of thought committed by some of his followers, I do not know. I suspect he was. In any event, as a sort of corrective to the rather one-sided picture of evolution which he had given in *The Origin of Species,* he published, in 1871, *The Descent of Man.* In this work he strongly emphasized the principle of co-operation and stated that "As man advances in civilization and small tribes are united into larger communities, the simplest reason would tell each individual that he ought to extend his social instinct and sympa-

23

thies to all members of the same nation, though personally unknown to him. This point being once reached, there is only an artificial barrier to prevent his sympathies extending to the men of all nations and races."

In *The Descent of Man* there was much else to the same effect, but Darwin's voice, together with that of many others which had been raised in protest against the crude, muscular Darwinian point of view, was drowned out in the din raised by the one-sided proponents of natural selection.

Activities which may collectively be called the struggle for existence do characterize the behavior of most animals, but such activities are not all that characterizes their behavior. Co-operative behavior is at least as prominent a form of interaction between animals, as we find them under so-called "natural" conditions, as is conflict or competition, the two forms of behavior, competition and cooperation, often complementing, rather than being in opposition to, each other. In what might be called the tough Darwinian period of the last century, the gladiatorial conception of evolution so completely dominated the thought of biologists and Spencerian sociologists—and practically every sociologist was a Spencerian in those days—that the existence of co-operative behavior on a large scale, though known to some biologists, was almost completely neglected in favor of the principle of natural selection. It was not that the Darwinists denied the existence of co-operation but that they neglected it in favor of a concept of natural selection which assumed too much, namely that life was a gladiatorial struggle for existence.

24

The extreme viewpoint of the natural selectionists was stated by Huxley in his article in 1888, to which reference has already been made. These views evoked a reply from Prince Petr Kropotkin in the form of eight articles published between 1890 and 1896 in the *Nineteenth Century*. These articles were published in book form in 1902 as *Mutual Aid a Factor in Evolution,* a work which made a deep impression upon all who read it.

In this work, Kropotkin attempted to show that there is an unconscious force throughout the realm of living nature which is expressed as an unconscious mutualism which serves to produce greater survival values for every form of life than would otherwise be the case. The unconscious recognition of this force, Kropotkin endeavored to show, serves to maintain each man in the practice of mutual aid. There is an unconscious recognition of the close dependency of everyone's happiness upon the happiness of all, and of the sense of justice or equity "which brings the individual to consider the rights of every other individual as equal to his own." [8]

Kropotkin's book was the first work of the twentieth century to set in motion all those ideas and investigations which by the middle of the twentieth century have taken shape in the principle of co-operation. Kropotkin's work also served the extremely useful purpose of drawing attention to the already considerable literature on the subject of co-operation in the animal world which emphasized an important and much underrated factor in evolution.

[8] These views were developed further in Kropotkin's *Ethics,* Dial Press, New York, 1924.

Lester Ward, the father of American sociology, in his *Dynamic Sociology* (1893), and Giddings, in *The Principles of Sociology* (1896), were among the first sociologists to emphasize the importance of co-operation in evolution, and, among English publicists, Henry Drummond chose for his Boston Lowell Lectures, published in 1894 as *The Ascent of Man*, the exposition of the thesis that, while in nature there was indeed a struggle for life, there was also such a thing as the struggle for the life of others. In the half-century since then, much work has been done in this field, so that today the principle of co-operation is in a fair way to becoming established as the most important factor in the survival of animal groups as of individuals.

Some of this evidence it must now be our task to set out and examine.

# The Social Appetite

---

*W*HILE DEFINITIONS ARE MORE MEANINGFUL AT THE END
of an inquiry than at the beginning, it may be of service at
this stage to say that by "life" is meant that condition in
which a body exhibits the functions of irritability (response to stimuli), motility (movement), and reproduc-
tivity (multiplication). An organism is that organization
of interactive elements which displays the functions of
life in a self-consistent manner. By "social" we mean all
those interactions between organisms or groups in which
needs are satisfied. By "cultural" is meant the particular
form which characterizes the social activities of a group.

In the early stages of life upon this earth, it is probable
that the only forms of life were represented by single-
celled plant and animal forms. In these forms of life the
single cell is a complete and self-supporting organism
which performs all the necessary vital functions for itself
by means of the differentiated parts of its protoplasmic
body. The amoeba and the paramecium are familiar examples of such unicellular organisms. These organisms
always originate from what might well be called a "par-

ent" cell. In this fact, at this early stage, may be perceived the fundamental ground of social life in the origin of one cell from another, in the relation of an "offspring" cell to the parent cell in the process of budding off or cleavage. *Omnis cellula e cellula*, every cell from a cell.

In amoeba, reproduction is effected by simple fission of the parent body into another single cell. The plant cell haematococcus (which often occurs in temporary pools of stagnant rainwater or in the resting condition in dried up mud or dust) multiplies itself by simple fission within the old cell wall, this process almost immediately resulting in the production of four new individuals (the same thing may happen in amoeba). Sometimes, however, another method of multiplication occurs in haematococcus. Instead of dividing into four relatively large zoospores, a restive individual may divide into thirty-two or sixty-four much smaller microzooids.

The microzooids freely swim about by means of their flagella, and sooner or later they come together in pairs, the members of each pair fusing with one another to form a single individual. This is an excellent illustration of sexual reproduction, the essential feature of which is the union or conjunction of two sexual cells, or gametes (in this case, the microzooids), to form a single cell, the zygote, which is the starting-point of a fresh series of cell generations.

Whether reproduction and multiplication are secured by fission or by conjugation of cells gametes, the process is always an interacting one between parent and developing new organism. The parent organism supplies the vital tissues to the new organism, and in the process of fission there are metabolic and other physiological exchanges before parent and offspring cells become organically independent of each other. This type of relationship, in varying degrees, is characteristic of all plant and animal life.

*It is here suggested that the fundamentally social nature of all living things has its origin in this physiological relationship between parent and offspring;* in the fact that the two are for a time bound together in an interactive association; that the life of either one or the other is at some time dependent upon the potential or actual being of the other. Thus, for example, when the amoeba has reached a certain size, the increase of tension becomes so great that it can only avoid death by dividing, and this it does. The original process of reproduction is a tension-reducing response. The new organism is, at least during the period of division, entirely dependent upon the proper functioning of its parent. In this dependency, brief as it may appear to our eyes, we may perceive the origins of infant dependency in the higher animals and the very obvious social, and, in man, cultural, consequences of that dependent relationship.

In short, it is suggested that *the universal fact of reproduction is the foundation of the social relationship which characterizes all living organisms,* indeed, that the primary co-operative act is the reproductive act. Where the offspring are born in a helpless condition and their post-natal care is more or less extended, we have a setting for the development of more complex forms of social life.

In the nature of the reproductive process we see, then, the basis for the development of social life, and the suggestion is that social life represents the response to organic drives, the expression of functions which are inextricably a part of the life of the organism.

In other words, the source of the social appetite of all living creatures is traceable to the way in which the living organism originates. All cells originate from other cells; it is impossible for them to originate in any other way. Whether reproduction is achieved by budding off or by cleavage, that is to say, asexually, or whether it is secured sexually, by the conjugation of cells, the process is always one of dependency and interdependency between parent and offspring. Dependency and interdependency are the indispensable conditions of life—and these are the conditions which all living organisms strive to maintain. All living organisms strive to be dependent and interdependent, because that is the living state—dependency and interdependency. Because the tissues of every organism remember their dependency and interdependency.

Each cell of the organism is dependent for its proper functioning upon the interaction with it of every other cell of the organism. Which is to say that every organism functions as a whole, and not as a mass of discrete, independent cellular elements. The organism is itself a dependent and interdependent whole.

No living organism is biologically solitary [4] in its

[4] "The growing weight of evidence indicates that animals are rarely solitary, that they are almost necessarily members of loosely integrated racial and interracial communities, in part woven together by environ-

origin and few are solitary in their lives. Most organisms, from the lowest to the highest, normally are to a certain extent engaged in some sort of social life. In this sense there is reason to believe that, with few exceptions, the solitary animal is, in any species, an abnormal creature. Under certain conditions, single animals are often observed, but to assume from such observation that such animals are necessarily "solitary," that is to say, that they spend most of their lives alone, is a very doubtful procedure indeed. The exceptions such as spiders and certain fishes are far from numerous. As Wheeler points out, "Most animals and plants live in associations, herds, colonies or societies and even the so-called 'solitary' species are obligatory, more or less co-operative members of groups or associations of individuals of different species." [5]

Examples of what has been called "the social appetite" in the lowest organisms have been known for many years. More than half a century ago, in 1894, the distinguished experimental embryologist, Wilhelm Roux, shook apart the cells of a frog's egg during an early stage of its development, placed the separated cells some distance apart in water, and watched to see what would happen. The separated cells slowly approached each other until they established contact.

---

mental factors, and in part by mutual attraction between the individual members of the different communities, no one of which can be affected without changing all the rest, at least to some extent." W. C. Allee, *The Social Life of Animals*, W. W. Norton, New York, 1938.
[5] W. M. Wheeler, *The Social Life of Insects*, Harcourt, Brace & Co., New York, 1922.

When an experimenter removes individual amoebae some distance from a group of their fellows, the separated amoebae immediately begin to make their way back to the group.

Deegener, in a series of experiments carried out on the caterpillar *Hyponomeuta* found that these creatures actively seek out the company of their fellows when separated from them, and that even the isolated larvae tend to seek out their kind. He recognizes a distinct need for association among caterpillars and speaks of a social instinct.[6]

Whether it is justifiable to speak of a social instinct with respect to caterpillars or whether it may not be that a tendency is present which under certain conditions leads to social behavior, the tendency to remain together is a fact.

It is a further fact that, with few exceptions, no animal avoids contact with its fellows, unless such contact under certain conditions happens to threaten it in some way. Under all other conditions, all animals exhibit a high tolerance for the presence of their kind. This does not for a moment imply that a type of social organization is developed by such elementary creatures, but rather that they exhibit potentialities for social life. It should always be remembered that in ascending the "scale of life" we are dealing with progressively increasing levels of integration, progressively increasing degrees of complexity, terminating in the most complex of all—in man. Nevertheless, in some very elementary forms of life, such as in

6 P. Deegener, "Soziologische Beobachtungen an Hyponomeuta cognatellus," *Hb. Biol. Centralbl.*, vol. 42, 1922, pp. 241-253.

certain bacteria, remarkable forms of what can only be regarded as social organization are seen.

As long ago as 1892, Thaxter showed that in Myxobacteria a remarkable specialization occurs which exhibits a striking division of labor in the service of the maintenance of the group. Individual bacteria held together in slime join to form a common nonreproductive stalk at the top of which numerous other bacteria join together in cystlike forms to propagate themselves.

Even earlier than this, in 1880, Van Tieghem found a more advanced type of social organization in the myxamoebae *Dictyostelium*. Here the myxamoebae derived from spores wander about freely and multiply separately. Subsequently all the members of the population come together and form a single aggregate, with the cells still maintaining their individuality. Then some of the cells become immobilized and transformed into stalk cells which are organized into a reproducing mass at the apex. From this position the matured spores become subsequently dispersed.

These are but a few of the innumerable examples which could be cited to demonstrate the existence of a social appetite throughout the kingdom of living forms. Whether we are dealing with fungi, bacteria, or higher plants and animals, the drive to form social aggregates is the same everywhere.

Some insects, fish, and at least one mammal, would appear to be exceptions to this rule. Pike and trout among fish, and the hyena among mammals, not only seem to prefer their own company but are frequently antagonistic to members of their own species. I strongly suspect that when the facts come to be thoroughly studied, these seeming exceptions will be found to prove the rule.

If the origin of social life owes its existence to the organic drives arising from the reproductive relationship, it is of more than passing interest to note that, physically, the multicellular organisms probably owe their origin to the same processes; that originally separate cells developed the habit of remaining attached together after division, as the spores in the encysted envelope of the parent amoeba might do to form a multicellular organism. Such an aggregation of cells would provide the means for the development of the multicellular higher animals. Such interactive cells would, by their increasing ability to co-operate, develop specialized functions and increasingly complex relations. The multicellular organism is therefore to be regarded as the expression of increasing intercellular co-operation in which the interdependent co-operating activities of its cellular masses function together so that at all times the organism is able to function as a unit and as a whole.

With the development of this interpretation of the facts, we reach the view not that society is an organism but that the organism is, in fact, a species of society. The organismal conception of society is today very generally discarded, yet while the notion of society as an organism may be difficult to justify, a strong case can be made out for the organism as a form of society. Every word in

34

Cooley's definition of society, for example, can be applied to the definition of an organism.

> Society is a complex of forms or processes each of which is living and growing by interaction with the others, the whole being so unified, that what takes place in one part affects all the rest. It is a vast tissue of reciprocal activity, differentiated into innumerable systems, some of them quite distinct, others not readily traceable, and all interwoven to such a degree that you see different systems according to the point of view you take.[7]

The system which a multicellular organism constitutes can also be so defined. But there is much more to human society than is stated in Cooley's definition, though that definition may serve as a description of society in general. It will not do as a definition of human society in particular because it omits any explicit reference to the fact that human society represents a development of mind, of interactive consciousnesses and the complex of relationships to which these give rise, in a sense quite different from that which might be conceived as possessed by the individual or masses of cells which are the interactive elements constituting the organism. The units constituting human society are comparatively free, those constituting the organism are, for the most part, fixed. The greater part of a society can be destroyed without causing the death of its remaining units, whereas, under similar conditions, death would generally follow in organisms. A person in human society exercises his will in a manner which is

[7] Charles H. Cooley, *The Social Process*, Scribner's, New York, 1918.

slightly, if at all, biologically predetermined, but which is largely culturally determined, and his unique being in thought, feeling, and action, again in a manner which is largely culturally influenced. This is not the case with regard to the cells which make up the organism.

All this is not to say that there is no relation between the society of the organism and human society, but simply that there is a very real difference between the two forms of society and that one must not be identified or confused with the other. The organismal analogy as applied to human society may be debatable, but the relationship of the behavior of the cells which in interaction constitute the organism and human society is a phylogenetic one, and this is far from being debatable.

Whatever the nature of the factors involved in the co-operation of cells cohering to form functioning many-celled organisms, such co-operation does exhibit the elements of a social act. The suggestion is that such acts originally represent the expression of a drive which has its origin in the nature of the reproductive-dependency relationship, further, that the tendency of living things to form societies is coeval with life itself, and finally, that human society represents the culmination of this tendency, and that in virtue of what seems to be the accident of the development of man's remarkable mental potentialities, his great plasticity, and freedom from biologically predetermined forms of behavior, human society has assumed a unique form, it has become culturalized.

The fact that such diverse groups as insects and mammals have developed social life indicates beyond any reasonable doubt the existence in organic life of deep-seated potentialities toward socialization, or what might properly be termed the process of forming society.

Having briefly sketched the case for the existence of a complex of organic drives or basic needs for co-operation in living organisms, we have now to inquire into the manner in which those drives or needs are expressed in some typical organisms, and further, to discover, if possible, what are the biological advantages, if any, of social as compared with solitary life.

# Aggregation versus Isolation

PROFESSOR WARDER C. ALLEE OF THE UNIVERSITY OF Chicago has summarized and presented the evidence that among the simpler plants and animals there exists a sort of unconscious co-operation, of automatic mutualism.[8] This co-operative behavior is primarily reflected in their tendency to aggregate, while the biological benefits which follow from their activities are exhibited in the significantly greater survival rate of organisms living in fairly dense populations than those living in sparse populations or in an environment in which they are isolated. Varying with the nature of the environments, the isolated animal will, in general, be retarded in growth or irremediably damaged or suffer death where the animal living in association with others will increase in size and in the speed of its physiological reactions, tend to recover quickly from wounds, and survive more often.

[8] W. C. Allee, *Animal Aggregations,* University of Chicago Press, 1931; Allee, *The Social Life of Animals,* W. W. Norton, New York, 1938; Allee and collaborators, *Principles of Animal Ecology,* Saunders, Philadelphia, 1949.

Thus planarian worms which had been exposed to ultra-violet radiation disintegrated more rapidly when isolated than when they were associated together. They survived exposure to ultra-violet radiation better when crowded while being radiated, and there was a much higher death rate among those which were isolated a few minutes after irradiation than among those which were left together. Goldfish placed together in groups of ten in a suspension of colloidal silver survived much longer than those which were placed in similar suspensions alone.

Allee writes

> When exposed to the toxic colloidal silver, the grouped fish shared between them a dose easily fatal for any one of them; the slime they secreted changed much of the silver into a less toxic form. In the experiment as set up, the suspension was somewhat too strong for any to survive; with a weaker suspension some or all of the grouped animals would have lived; as it was, the group gained for its members a longer life. In nature they could have had many more minutes for rain to have diluted the water or some other disturbance to have cleared up the poison and given the fish a chance for complete recovery.

This latter experiment illustrates in the case of goldfish —and presumably holds true for all other aquatic organisms—the physicochemical basis of the advantage which lies in numbers. Allee's studies on the rate of cleavage of the fertilized egg of the common sea urchin, arbacia, show that, with few exceptions, the rate is more rapid in the denser clusters of eggs than in unclustered or isolated fellow eggs. Protozoans, it has been experimentally shown, grow more rapidly when they are introduced in large numbers into a sterile medium of relatively simple salts than if the cultures are started with only a few organisms. The biological advantages are all in the crowding—not overcrowding—while separation or isolation would appear to be so fatal to the organism that we can be fairly certain that as a way of life it rarely, if ever, occurs in nature.

What is an optimal population size for different groups in nature will depend upon the group and its environment, but thus far the evidence strongly indicates that optimal numbers present in a given situation have certain positive survival values and definitely exert stimulating effects on the growth of individuals and the increase of populations.[9] Thus, for example, Darling has found that among herring gulls the members of larger colonies stimulate each other to commence sexual activities earlier than when the colonies are smaller, and furthermore, there tends to be a speeding up of egg-laying, so that breeding activities are more intense while they last. The value of the short spread of time between laying and hatching lies in the fact that a greater number of young gulls survive under such conditions than in the case where the colony is small and the spread of hatching time therefore longer.[10]

The unconscious kind of mutualism or co-operation which universally exists among lower animals, not com-

[9] W. C. Allee, *The Social Life of Animals*. W. W. Norton & Co., 1938.
[10] Fraser Darling, *Bird Flocks and the Breeding Cycle*, Cambridge University Press, New York, 1938.

monly regarded as social or viewed only as partially social, undoubtedly represents an earlier stage in the development of social life among the higher animals. It is important to understand in its full implications the fact that this principle of co-operation is the fundamental principle which appears to have governed the relations of organisms from the very first, and we have attempted to show that the organic basis for this is to be found in the nature of the reproductive relationship, with the accompanying mutual interrelations which are for a time maintained between parent and developing organism.

At the present time the principle of co-operation is in a fair way to becoming recognized as the most important factor in the survival of animal groups. Summing up the modern point of view, Allee says:

> After much consideration, it is my mature conclusion, contrary to Herbert Spencer, that the co-operative forces are biologically the more important and vital. The balance between the co-operative and altruistic tendencies and those which are disoperative and egoistic is relatively close. Under many conditions the co-operative forces lose. In the long run, however, the group centered, more altruistic drives are slightly stronger. If co-operation had not been the stronger force, the more complicated animals, whether arthropods or vertebrates, could not have evolved from simpler ones, and there would have been no men to worry each other with their distressing and biologically foolish wars. While I know of no laboratory experiments that make a direct test of this problem, I have come to this conclusion by

41

studying the implications of many experiments which bear on both sides of the problem and from considering the trends of organic evolution in nature. Despite many known appearances to the contrary, human altruistic drives are as firmly based on an animal ancestry as is man himself. Our tendencies toward goodness, such as they are, are as innate as our tendencies toward intelligence; we could do well with more of both.[11]

The tendentious habit of thinking of evolution in terms of the struggle for existence, by means of which, it is believed, the "fittest" are alone selected for survival while the weakest are ruthlessly condemned to extinction, is not only an incorrect view of the facts but is a habit of thought which has done a considerable amount of harm. Only by omitting any reference to such an important evolutionary force as the principle of co-operation, and by viewing evolution as a process of continuous conflict between all living things, can men be led to conclude that survival or development depends on successful aggression. Omitting important facts and basing their arguments on false premises, the tough Darwinians could only arrive at false conclusions. As Allee says, "Today, as in Darwin's time, the average biologist apparently still thinks of a natural selection which acts primarily on egoistic principles, and intelligent fellow thinkers in other disciplines, together with the much-cited man-in-the-street, cannot be blamed for taking the same point of view." [12]

11 Warder C. Allee, "Where Angels Fear to Tread: A Contribution From General Sociology to Human Ethics," *Science*, vol. 97, 1943, p. 521.
12 *Ibid.*, 520.

Certainly, aggressiveness [13] exists in nature, but there is also a healthy nonruthless competition, and there exist very strong drives toward social and co-operative behavior. These forces do not operate independently but together, as a whole, and the evidence strongly indicates that, of all these drives, the principle of co-operation is the most dominant, and biologically the most important. The co-existence of so many different species of animals throughout the world is a sufficient testimony to the importance of that principle. It is probable that man owes more to the operation of this principle than to any other in his own biological and social evolution. Indeed, without this principle of co-operation, of sociability and mutual aid, the progress of organic life, the improvement of the organism, and the strengthening of the species become utterly incomprehensible.

We may, by induction from the facts, arrive at a generalization to the effect that the greater the co-operative behavior exhibited by the members of any group, the more harmoniously socially organized is that group likely to be. Interesting examples of this are the social ants, in which the principle of co-operation has been developed to the

[13] The terms "aggressiveness," "conflict" and "combativeness" should be distinguished. All drives may be said to be aggressive. Aggressiveness should not be equated with hostility. It is possible to be aggressive without being either hostile, combative, competitive, or conflict-producing. Aggression may be co-operative. It may be defined as the outward direction of energy. See I. Hendricks, "Instincts and the Ego During Infancy," *Psychoanalytic Quarterly*, vol. 11, 1942, pp. 33-59; and L. Bender, "Genesis of Hostility in Children," *American Journal of Psychiatry*, vol. 105, 1948, pp. 241-245.

limit of fixity. Yet, as Schneirla has suggested, it would perhaps be more accurate to speak of *bio-social facilitation* rather than of co-operation here because of the psychological limitations of social ants.[14]

The distinction is, however, simply one of organization at qualitatively different levels. The principle of co-operation has been resumed by a group of distinguished biologists in the statement that the probability of survival of individual or living things increases with the degree in which they harmoniously adjust themselves to each other and to their environment.[15]

Today, contrary to the "Nature, red in tooth and claw" school of natural selectionists, the evidence increasingly indicates that natural selection does not act principally to favor variations which better adjust the organism to its environment. Such adjustment is, of course, necessary, but the important point is that natural selection favors the co-operative, as opposed to the disoperative, struggling for survival. As Burkholder has recently stated, "The most important basis for selection is the ability of associated components to work together harmoniously in the organism and among organisms. All new genetic factors, whether they arise from within by mutation or are incorporated from without by various means, are accepted or

14 T. C. Schneirla, "Problems in the Biopsychology of Social Organization," *Journal of Abnormal and Social Psychology*, vol. 41, 1946, pp. 385-402.
15 C. Leake, "Ethicogenesis," *Proceedings of the Philosophical Society of Texas*, vol. 10, 1944, pp. 7-34. See also a revision of this article in *Studies and Essays in the History of Science and Learning* (ed. by M. F. Ashley Montagu), Schuman, New York, 1946, pp. 261-275.

rejected according to their co-operation with associated components in the whole aggregation." [16]

We begin to understand, then, that evolution itself is a process which favors co-operating rather than disoperating groups, and "fitness" is a function of the group as a whole rather than of separate individuals. The fitness of the individual is largely derived from his membership in a group. The more co-operative the group, the greater is the fitness for survival which extends to all its members. As A. E. Emerson has concluded, the dominant directional trend in evolution is toward a controlled balance of the important factors within the system. "Human society co-operatively brings the social environment under control for the better survival of the species." [17]

If we would seek for one word which describes society better than any other, that word is co-operation. The important point to grasp is that, contrary to the beliefs of the struggle-for-survival school of thought, man does not have to create a co-operative mood for himself to erect over the tufa of his savage strivings to be otherwise. Not at all. The impulses toward co-operative behavior are already present in him at birth, and all they require is cultivation. There is not a shred of evidence that man is born with "hostile" or "evil" impulses which must be watched and disciplined. Discipline of basic impulses is, indeed,

[16] P. R. Burkholder, "Co-operation and Conflict Among Primitive Organisms," Typescript.
[17] A. E. Emerson, "The Biological Basis of Social Co-operation," *Illinois Academy of Science Transactions*, vol. 39, 1946.

necessary, but it is the discipline of love, *not* of frustration, which they require.

Indeed, in so far as any of its strivings are concerned, the infant of most birds and mammals is equipped with the ability to compete with the universe for attention, and it generally succeeds in eliciting co-operative behavior, usually from one or both parents.

In the process of socialization, a certain quantity of the energies of aggressiveness are transformed into co-operative processes. The reproductive process is a co-operative one, and, in addition, development as one of a litter or group of siblings represents another early experience in the development of co-operation; development within a family represents a still further experience in the learning and practice of co-operation.

So far we have been trying to establish the fact that some degree of social life is present in even the lowest organisms, and that such a thing as a completely asocial variety of animal probably does not exist. This would seem to be the first point to grasp in arriving at any understanding of the nature of what is social. The second point is that social life confers distinct biological advantages upon the animals participating in it. Allee and Emerson, indeed, regard as at least partially social any group in which the animals confer distinct survival values upon each other. Thirdly, the dominant principle of social life is not the struggle for existence, but co-operation is. Fourthly, the evidence indicates that some form of social life is probably coeval with life itself, otherwise life could not have become established. And finally, the organic basis of social behavior is to be found in the nature of the reproductive relationship between maternal genitor and offspring. It is of great significance that the reproductive process which is concerned with the creation of life itself should constitute the fundamental social relationship and that in the evolution of living organisms, from the simple to the complex, mutually beneficial mass physiological interactions continue to form the organic basis of social life. Man is no exception to this rule, but he is the one animal most capable of modifying it by means of his culturally inherited devices and own social inventions.

The answer to our first question, "What is the nature of life?" can be expressed in one word, co-operation—the interaction between organisms for mutual support in such a way as to confer survival benefits upon each other. Another word for the same thing, as we shall see in the pages which follow, is love. Without co-operation, without love, it is not possible to live—at best, it is possible only to exist.

# 2

# What Is the Nature of Human Nature?

---

# The Basic Needs of Man

Mᴀɴ ᴀs ᴀɴ ᴀɴɪᴍᴀʟ ᴍᴜsᴛ ʙʀᴇᴀᴛʜᴇ, ᴇᴀᴛ, ᴅʀɪɴᴋ, excrete, sleep, maintain adequate health, and procreate. These basic physiological needs constitute the minimum biological conditions which must be satisfied by any human group if its members are to survive. They and their functioning interrelations constitute the innate nature of man. Second nature is that organization of cultural conditionings which is imposed upon, and more or less integrated with, the primary innate needs of man.

A basic need may be defined as any urge or need of the organism which must be satisfied if the organism or the group is to survive.

The table below lists the basic vital needs and may be read as follows: The physiological tension of oxygen hunger represents the urge or need to intake air. It is an imperative need, one which must be satisfied if the organism is to survive. This need usually leads to the act of breathing, a satisfying act in itself, and this usually results in oxygenation of the tissues of the body, a replenishment of energy, and a restoration to equilibrium, homeostasis. It is to be noted that the act of breathing is part of the

51

## THE BASIC NEEDS AND THEIR VITAL SEQUENCES

| | | S A T I S F A C T I O N | |
|---|---|---|---|
| *Physiological Tension* | = $\begin{cases} \textit{Urge or} \\ \textit{Need to} \rightarrow \end{cases}$ | *Which Leads to the Act of* $\rightarrow$ | *Homeostasis* |
| Oxygen hunger | = $\begin{cases} \text{intake} \rightarrow \\ \text{air} \end{cases}$ | breathing $\rightarrow$ | oxygenation of tissues |
| Hunger | = $\begin{cases} \text{ingest} \rightarrow \\ \text{food} \end{cases}$ | ingesting food $\rightarrow$ | satiation |
| Thirst | = $\begin{cases} \text{intake} \rightarrow \\ \text{liquid} \end{cases}$ | intaking liquid $\rightarrow$ | quenching |
| Sex | = $\begin{cases} \text{conju-} \rightarrow \\ \text{gate} \end{cases}$ | conjugation $\rightarrow$ | detumescence |
| Fatigue | = $\begin{cases} \text{rest} \rightarrow \end{cases}$ | resting $\rightarrow$ | restoration of muscular and nervous organization |
| Restlessness | = $\begin{cases} \text{be ac-} \rightarrow \\ \text{tive} \end{cases}$ | activity $\rightarrow$ | reduction of energy to equilibrium |
| Somnolence | = $\begin{cases} \text{sleep} \rightarrow \end{cases}$ | sleeping $\rightarrow$ | awakening with restored energy |
| Bladder pressure | = $\begin{cases} \text{mictu-} \rightarrow \\ \text{rate} \end{cases}$ | micturating $\rightarrow$ | tension removal |
| Colon pressure | = $\begin{cases} \text{defe-} \rightarrow \\ \text{cate} \end{cases}$ | defecation $\rightarrow$ | removal tension |
| Fright | = $\begin{cases} \text{escape} \rightarrow \end{cases}$ | escaping from danger $\rightarrow$ | relaxation |
| Pain | = $\begin{cases} \text{avoid} \rightarrow \end{cases}$ | avoidance $\rightarrow$ | return to normal state |
| Internal Excitation | = $\begin{cases} \text{Crav-} \rightarrow \\ \text{ing} \end{cases}$ | Neuromuscular Act | Equilibrium |

process of satisfaction and that the replenishment of the tissues with the necessary energy for their proper functioning is the end effect. And so on for the rest of the basic vital sequences.

In addition to the vital basic needs, the satisfaction of which is necessary if the individual and the group are to survive, there are several nonvital basic needs which must be satisfied if the organism is to develop and maintain adequate mental health. These nonvital basic needs have their origin in the same kinds of physiological states as do the vital basic needs. Two of these nonvital basic needs may be schematized as follows:

| Physiological Tension | | Urge or Need to | | Which Leads to the Act of | | Homeostasis |
|---|---|---|---|---|---|---|
| | | | | SATISFACTION | | |
| Feeling of non-dependency or aloneness | = | be with others | → | physical contact or association | → | feeling of security or interdependency |
| General need or tension | = | expression | → | communication | → | social recognition |

The tension of nondependency is doubtless connected in the continuum of life (phylogenetically) with the parent-offspring relationship which is characteristic of all living things, and in the individual history of the person (ontogenetically) is associated with his prolonged sojourn within the womb. During these phases of its existence, within the womb and during infancy, the organism is *dependent* upon the maternal organism for the satisfaction of its needs.

Dependency is the state of reliance of the organism upon objects outside itself for the satisfaction of its needs.

In brief, dependency is the state of striving to obtain support from sources external to the organism. The directiveness of drives is, therefore, outward in order to obtain gratification of needs from objects stimulated by the appropriate acts.

All needs are dependent. They must therefore be satisfied by some object or objects. An attempt will be made here to show that those needs must always be satisfied in the manner which they require, and furthermore, that their requirements are such that they dictate the manner in which they must be satisfied if the organism is to function as a healthy whole. Indeed, it will be shown that the facts of man's biological nature, what *is*, determine the direction his development as a person must take. That is to say, that what *is* here clearly determines what *ought to be;* in short, that the biological facts give a biological validation to the principle of co-operation, or love, in human life. In other words, we can here demonstrate that there are certain values for human life which are not matters of opinion but which are biologically determined. If we do violence to those determinants, we disorder our lives, as persons, as groups, as nations, and as a world of human beings whose biological drives are directed toward love, toward co-operation. If we can clearly grasp the meaning of the facts, and they are easily understood, we shall the more readily be in a position to put them to practical use. Let us to the facts, then.

# The First Step

*T*HE INFANT, AT BIRTH, IS EQUIPPED WITH ACTIVE DRIVES
to receive love from the mother. Here the first fulfillment
of these drives is a fundamental co-operative act. As Alfred Adler has pointed out, "the first act of a new-born
child—drinking from the mother's breast—is co-operation,
and is as pleasant for the mother as for the child." [18] There
is the tactile stimulation about the lips and face, the
tongue, the oral cavity, and the liquid stimulation of the
gastro-intestinal tract. Here, in this act, is the first step
in the development of the sense of contact with another
person. In Adler's words:

> . . . the child's inclination to co-operation is challenged
> from the very first day. The immense importance of the
> mother in this respect can be clearly recognized. She
> stands on the threshold of the development of social
> feeling. The biological heritage of social feeling is en-
> trusted to her charge. She can strengthen or hinder con-
> tact by the help she gives the child in little things, in

[18] A. Adler, *Social Interest: A Challenge to Mankind*, Putnam's, New
York, 1938.

bathing him, in providing all that a helpless infant is in need of. Her relations with the child, her knowledge, and her aptitude are decisive factors. . . . It may readily be accepted that contact with the mother is of the highest importance for the development of human social feeling. . . . *We probably owe to the maternal sense of contact the largest part of human social feeling, and along with it the essential continuance of human civilization.*[19]

Frustration of the drives to receive love from the mother (not necessarily the biological mother, a mother surrogate will do) at this period not only produces anxiety in the infant but also a retention of unexpressed hunger for tangible mother love, which may then find an outlet through gastro-intestinal disease. Similarly, if the infant's cries for attention remain unanswered, the unsatisfied tensions may express themselves through the bronchial tree in the form of asthma.[20] Such responses constitute involuntary emergency discharges through the organ systems involved in the frustration of the need. The energies which should have been discharged outward are now discharged inward.[21] The affection of the organ or organ systems becomes a substitute affect-equivalent for the original gratification sought by the organism. A large proportion of, if not all, neuroses and psychosomatic

[19] *Ibid.*
[20] F. Alexander, "Psychogenic Factors in Bronchial Asthma," Part I, *Psychosomatic Medicine Monograph*, IV, 1941, p. 58.
[21] For a discussion of the organ neuroses, see O. Fenichel, *The Psychoanalytic Theory of the Neuroses*, W. W. Norton, New York, 1945, pp. 236-267.

disorders may be so explained—their foundations being laid within the first six years of life.

The importance of love in the early social development of the infant cannot be overemphasized. Its real significance can best be understood when we consider a disease from which, but half a century ago, more than half the children in their first year of life regularly died. This disease was known as marasmus, from the Greek word meaning "wasting away." The disease was also known as infantile atrophy or debility. When intensive studies were undertaken to track down its cause, the discovery was made that babies in the best homes and hospitals were most often its victims, babies who were apparently receiving the best and most careful physical attention, while babies in the poorest homes, with a good mother, despite the lack of hygienic physical conditions, often overcame the physical handicaps and flourished. What was wanting in the sterilized environment of the babies of the first class and was generously supplied in babies of the second class was mother love.

This discovery is responsible for the fact that hospitals today endeavor to keep the infant for as short a period as possible. The best place for the infant is with its mother, and if its own mother is not available, with a foster mother, for what the infant must have is love. Drs. Ruth and Harry Bakwin, pediatricians of great experience, point out that:

> The effect of residence in a hospital manifests itself by a fairly well-defined clinical picture. A striking feature

is the failure to gain properly, despite the ingestion of diets which are entirely adequate for growth in the home. Infants in hospitals sleep less than others and they rarely smile or babble spontaneously. They are listless and apathetic and look unhappy. The appetite is indifferent and food is accepted without enthusiasm. The stools tend to be frequent and, in sharp contrast with infants cared for in the home, it is unusual for 24 hours to pass without an evacuation. Respiratory infections which last only a day or two in the home are prolonged and may persist for weeks or months. Return to the home results in defervesence [disappearance of fever] within a few days and a prompt and striking gain in weight.[22]

The emotional deprivation suffered by infants in hospitals may do vastly more damage than the physical condition which brought them there. The infant can suffer no greater loss than the privation of its mother's love, for it would seem that the satisfaction of the generalized feeling of dependency, in itself a basic need, is best accomplished through mother-love. Because the mother is the person usually most profoundly interested in the welfare of her infant, it is from her that the infant receives the supports and reassurances which love bestows. This is not to say that some other person not the mother of the infant could not do as much for it. There is good reason to believe that devoted foster mothers or nurses have often successfully taken the place of the actual mother

[22] Ruth M. Bakwin and Harry Bakwin, *Psychologic Care During Infancy and Childhood*, Appleton-Century Co., New York, 1942, p. 295.

in giving the infant all the love it required. Normally, however, the infant receives its love from the person best qualified to give it, the biological mother.

Now let us see what is likely to happen to the infant who is deprived of his mother shortly after birth. An illuminating example is the following case, described by Dr. Margaret Ribble:

> Little Bob was born in the maternity hospital where the writer was making studies of infants at the time. He was a full-term child and weighed six pounds three ounces at birth. During the two weeks' stay in the hospital the baby was breast fed and there was no apparent difficulty with his body functions. The mother, a professional woman, had been reluctant about breast feeding because she wished to take up her work as soon as possible after the baby was born, but she yielded to the kindly encouragement of the hospital nurses, and the feeding was successful. Both mother and child were thriving when they left the hospital.
>
> On returning home, the mother found that her husband had suddenly deserted her—the climax of an unhappy and maladjusted marriage relationship. She discovered soon after that her milk did not agree with the baby. As is frequently the case, the deep emotional reaction had affected her milk secretion. The infant refused the breast and began to vomit. Later he was taken to the hospital and the mother did not call to see him. At the end of a month she wrote that she had been seriously ill and asked the hospital to keep the child until further notice.
>
> In spite of careful medical attention and skillful feed-

ing, this baby remained for two months at practically the same weight. He was in a crowded ward and received very little personal attention. The busy nurses had no time to take him up and work with him as a mother would, by changing his position and making him comfortable at frequent intervals. The habit of finger sucking developed, and gradually the child became what is known as a ruminator, his food coming up and going down with equal ease. At the age of two months he weighed five pounds. The baby at this time was transferred to a small children's hospital, with the idea that this institution might be able to give him more individual care. It became apparent that the mother had abandoned the child altogether.

When seen by the writer, this baby actually looked like a seven months' foetus yet he had also a strange appearance of oldness. His arms and legs were wrinkled and wasted, his head large in proportion to the rest of his body, his chest round and flaring widely at the base over an enormous liver. His breathing was shallow, he was generally inactive, and his skin was cold and flabby. He took large quantities of milk, but did not gain weight since most of it went through him with very little assimilation and with copious discharges of mucus from his intestines. The baby showed at this time the pallor which in our study we have found typical of infants who are not mothered, although careful examination of his blood did not indicate a serious degree of anemia. He was subject to severe sweating, particularly during sleep. A thorough study showed no indication of tuberculosis. The child's abdomen was large and protruding, but this proved to be due to lax intestinal mus-

cles and consequent distention with gas and to a greatly
enlarged and distended liver, which was actually in proportion to that of the foetus. There was no evidence of
organic disease, but growth and development were definitely at a standstill, and it appeared that the child was
gradually slipping backward to lower and lower levels
of body economy and function.

The routine treatment for this hospital for babies
who are not gaining weight is to give them concen-
trated nursing care. They are held in the nurses' laps
for feeding and allowed at least half an hour to take the
bottle. From time to time their position in the crib is
changed and when possible the nurse carries them about
the ward for a few minutes before or after each feeding.
This is the closest possible approach to mothering in a
busy infants' ward. Medical treatment consists of frequent injections of salt solution under the skin to support the weakened circulation in the surface of the
body.

With this treatment the child began to improve
slowly. As his physical condition became better, it was
possible for our research group to introduce the services
of a volunteer "mother" who came to the hospital twice
daily in order to give him some of the attention he so
greatly needed. What she actually did was to hold him
in her lap for a short period before his 10 A.M. and 6 P.M.
feedings. She was told that he needed love more than
he needed medicine, and she was instructed to stroke
the child's head gently and speak or sing softly to him
and walk him about. Her daily visits were gradually
prolonged until she was spending an hour twice a day,
giving the baby this artificial mothering. The result was

good. The child remained in the hospital until it was five months of age, at which time he weighed nine pounds. All rumination and diarrhea had stopped, and he had become an alert baby with vigorous muscular activity. His motor coordinations were of course retarded. Although he held up his head well and looked about, focussing his eyes and smiling in response to his familiar nurses, he could not yet grasp his own bottle or turn himself over, as is customary at this age. The finger sucking continued, as is usually the case with babies who have suffered early privation.

In accordance with the new hospital procedure, as soon as the child's life was no longer in danger, he was transferred to a good, supervised foster home in order that he might have still more individual attention. Under this regime, his development proceeded well and gradually he mastered such functions as sitting, creeping, and standing. His speech was slow in developing, however, and he did not walk until after the second year. The general health of this child is now excellent at the end of his third year, also his "I.Q." is high on standard tests, but his emotional life is deeply damaged. With any change in his routine or with a prolonged absence of the foster mother, he goes into a state which is quite similar to a depression. He becomes inactive, eats very little, becomes constipated and extremely pale. When his foster mother goes away, he usually reacts with a loss of body tone and alertness, rather than with a definite protest. His emotional relationship to the foster mother is receptive, like that of a young infant, but he makes little response to her mothering activities except to function better when she is there. He has little capacity to express affection which he so deeply needs. Without the constant friendly explanations of the situation from the visiting nurse, she would probably have given up the care of the child.[23]

Evidence gathered by many investigators renders it highly probable that to a greater or lesser extent the history of the emotional development of this child represents the history of most unmothered infants. The history of this child is by no means extreme, but it does illustrate, rather strikingly, the effects upon the newborn and infant of the absence of the stimulus which a mother's love provides. Without that stimulus, the psychosomatic effects upon the child are often disastrous. Such a child may be emotionally crippled for life. As adults, such children remain fixated at their early dependent, infantile level, they demand affection but cannot easily return it.

Studies carried out on children who have spent their infancy in institutions lead to the conclusion, in Lowrey's words, that such infants—

. . . undergo an isolation type of experience with resulting isolation type of personality, characterized by unsocial behavior, hostile aggression, lack of patterns for giving and receiving affection, inability to understand and accept limitations, much insecurity in adapting to environment. These children present delays in development and intensification as well as prolongation of behavior manifestations at these levels. At the time of transfer (to a foster home), the children are at a stage

[23] Margaret Ribble, *The Rights of Infants,* Columbia University Press, New York, 1943, pp. 4-7.

when they can form only partial love attachments; hostility and aggression are at a peak; egocentricity is marked, and they do not recognize the individuality and needs of others. They are unprepared for and unequal to the demands and limitations of a family setting. They are exposed to attention and affection far in excess of anything they have previously known, and react excessively either by extravagant behavior, negativism or both.[24]

The work of Goldfarb as well as of others has demonstrated conclusively that the institutionally reared child is characterized by a personality which is strikingly less differentiated than that of the home-reared child. Such children are markedly more passive and apathetic as a consequence, presumably, of their highly routinized experience. Motivation and ambition is lacking. Language retardation is severe and persists well into adolescence. Aggressive behavior and instability of emotional response is usual, and deficiencies of inhibition the rule. They are restless, aimless in their behavior, unreflective, and lacking in persistence. The impoverished social environment of the institution, the lack of a dynamic and varied social experience, is reflected in the inability of the institutionalized child to develop meaningful reciprocal human relationships. The lack of loving attention, affection, and stimulation of the family, with its human protecting and supporting ties, in the experience of such children leads to a marked insecurity with a resulting hunger for atten-

[24] Lawson G. Lowrey, "Personality Distortion and Early Institutional Care," *American Journal of Orthopsychiatry*, vol. 10, 1935, pp. 576-585.

tion and affection. In the younger children attention-seeking behavior is particularly marked, and this is usually combined with hostile, overtly aggressive acts. Eventually, the conflict between the need for affection and the inability to respond to normal human relationships is resolved by a more consistent defense of emotional isolation, resulting in apathetic social responses and a pattern of withdrawal from life's tasks.[25]

Such children, while they may improve following adoption into a family, never recover from the effects of their early deprivations. It is not difficult to recognize such persons in adulthood. The basic personality defects are congealed at a level of extreme immaturity. By the age of six years, the damage has been effectively done that will mar the institution child for the rest of his life.

As Goldfarb points out, "Under normal circumstances, early dependency becomes the constructive basis for the development of a growing and secure sense of independ-

[25] For the best account of research findings on the personality of the institutionalized child, see William Goldfarb, "The Effects of Early Institutional Care on Adolescent Personality," *Journal of Experimental Education*, vol. 12, 1943, pp. 106-129; also the following papers by the same author, "Infant Rearing and Problem Behavior," *American Journal of Orthopsychiatry*, vol. 13, 1943, pp. 249-265; "The Effects of Early Institutional Care on Adolescent Personality (Graphic Rorschach Data)," *Child Development*, vol. 14, 1943, pp. 213-223; "Infant Rearing as a Factor in Foster Home Replacement," *American Journal of Orthopsychiatry*, vol. 14, 1944, pp. 162-166; "Psychological Privation in Infancy and Subsequent Adjustment," *American Journal of Orthopsychiatry*, vol. 15, 1945, pp. 247-255; "Effects of Psychological Deprivation in Infancy and Subsequent Stimulation," *American Journal of Psychiatry*, vol. 102, 1945, pp. 18-33.

ence. In other words, independence is a positive and mature adaptation based on secure grasp of the self in relation to other people. This is to be differentiated from the isolation reaction of the institution group, for the latter reaction represents defensive adaptation to a confused, hazy, and thus fearful grasp of one's relationship to the world of people and things as well as to inadequate methods for meeting reality." [26]

The dependency needs normally satisfied by the mother are in institution children *inadequately* satisfied, and the result is a more or less permanent failure of development of the affective life of the person.

It is important to note that *inadequate* satisfaction of the dependency needs, *not* complete deprivation, is sufficient to produce this failure of affective development. It appears that the damage done is related to the degree of privation suffered by the infant. For example, rejected children will show very similar symptoms to institution children. The differences, however, are very significant, varying with the conditions.

The deprivation situation is characterized by a marked poverty of affective and social stimulation. In the institution child this is further reinforced by the handicapping barrenness and narrowness of the institution environment. The world of things and of people, of experience as something lived or undergone, is flattened out and severely limited. The interstimulation of family relation-

[26] William Goldfarb, "The Effects of Early Institutional Care on Adolescent Personality," *Journal of Experimental Education*, vol. 12, 1943, p. 128.

ships in all their manifold aspects is lost. And as Goldfarb so well puts it, "The institution child thus establishes no specific identifications and engages in no meaningful reciprocal relationships with the people. The basic motivations to normal maturation and differentiation of personality are absent. Paucity in content and organization of both intellect and feeling follow. The ego structure is primitive and undeveloped. . . . Both the 'I' of the inner life, and the 'It' of the outer life, are crippled." [27]

On the other hand, while the rejected child may suffer from a greater or lesser degree of affective deprivation, the horizon of its experience is usually nowhere nearly as limited as that of the institution child. Hence, the rejected child does not usually exhibit any defects in abstract thinking as does the institution child; his span of attention and his concentrative powers are not as crippled. He is more anxious, more ambitiously purposeful, and has a much greater capacity for insight. He therefore usually responds to treatment, whereas the institution child rarely responds effectively.

It is possible that there are some homes in which the rejection of a child has been so extreme as to produce symptoms in it of deprivation identical with those of the institution child. This is an area of social pathology which requires further investigation.

So far as the effects of varying forms of privation upon the personality are concerned, the evidence now available

[27] William Goldfarb, "Psychological Privation in Infancy and Subsequent Adjustment," *American Journal of Orthopsychiatry*, vol. 15, 1945, p. 254.

for nonliterate and other peoples is extremely suggestive.

In Western societies there are great variations in the kind and amount of mothering which infants receive. Class differences here play an important role. Among the upper classes the mother tends to shift the burden of "mothering" the infant to a nurse as soon as possible. In Europe and, until very recently, in the South, upper-class children were almost always brought up by nurses and governesses. In the middle classes, the mother tended to care for her own child a good deal of the time, at least during the newborn and infancy periods, even though a nurse or governess was also employed. Among the lower classes universally the mother is the person who gives the child most attention. To what extent these differences in "mothering" affect the development of personality is a matter for future research to determine. It is possible that such differences in "mothering" in the early months and years of life will be found to have a profound effect on character.

In this particular field we need more research studies. It will not be enough to inquire into the personality development of unmothered children, though this is indispensable. It is also highly desirable to discover the variation in mothering which different mothers have given their children, and to inquire into the exact amount and quality of mothering the person has received from the mother and how much from nurses and other persons.

The upper-class Englishman (and Englishwoman) may prove to be good material for the investigation of this problem. Over and beyond the fact that the early training and inhibitions of the upper-class Englishman prevent him from ever exhibiting much emotion, there is detectable a certain lack of warmth which, in common with the members of the upper classes of other nations, may be found to be due to an early lack of mothering. Not all members of the upper classes exhibit this lack of warmth and many members of the middle and lower classes may show it. This lack of warmth in adults often signifies the inability to love other persons, and in such adults one usually looks in vain for that human sympathy with others which one finds in most human beings. It may seem a bit far-fetched to suggest that the ability of the upper middle, and upper-class Englishman to rule and govern subject peoples and to justify that rule, has, in the past at least, to some extent been due to such lack of sympathetic understanding for others.[28]

The custom among the upper and upper middle classes in England of sending their children away to boarding schools at an early age, of institutionalizing them, as it were, outside the warm ambience of the family, deprives these children of the love and affection which is necessary for the healthy development of the personality. This privation of parental love suffered during the tender years of childhood is probably one of the causes of the apparent "coldness," the seemingly unemotional character of the upper-class Englishman. On this aspect of the Eng-

[28] For some interesting comments bearing upon these points, see Geoffrey Gorer, "Some Notes on the British Character," *Horizon*, vol. 20, 1949/50, pp. 369-379.

lishman's character, E. M. Forster has an interesting passage:

> People talk of the mysterious East, but the West also is mysterious. It has depths that do not reveal themselves at the first glance. We know what the sea looks like from a distance; it is of one color, and level, and obviously cannot contain such creatures as fish. But if we look into the sea over the edge of a boat, we see a dozen colors, and depth below depth, and fish swimming in them. That sea is the English character—apparently imperturbable and even. The depths and the colors are the English romanticism and the English sensitiveness—we do not expect to find such things, but they exist. And— to continue my metaphor—the fish are the English emotions, which are always trying to get up to the surface, but don't quite know how. For the most part we see them moving far below, distorted and obscure. Now and then they succeed and we exclaim, "Why, the Englishman has emotions! He actually can feel!" And occasionally we see that beautiful creature, the flying fish, which rises out of the water altogether into the air and sunlight. English literature is a flying fish. It is a sample of the life that goes on day after day beneath the surface; it is a proof that beauty and emotion exist in the salt, inhospitable sea.[29]

Quite in contrast to the Englishman's emotional restraint is the emotional warmth and sensitivity of, say, the Italian or the Russian. It is significant that the Italian

[29] E. M. Forster, *Abinger Harvest*, Harcourt, Brace, New York, 1947. For a beautiful exemplification of the type, see Timothy Eden, *The Tribulations of a Baronet*, Macmillan, London, 1933.

or Russian family is one in which the members are closely bound to one another in a loving, emotional atmosphere which is very different from that found among English-speaking peoples. In pre-Bolshevik Russia it was very generally considered a tragedy for a Russian girl to entertain the idea of marrying an Englishman—"cold fish" apparently utterly incapable of all emotion! The Italians still entertain similar views concerning the English—not altogether unjustifiably.

# No Man Is an Island

In all the examples of failure of one kind or another in the process of mothering, of satisfaction of basic needs, we perceive as the end effect the failure to develop social competence, for social interaction is simply the extension of mother-child interaction, and the ability of the person to interact socially will depend largely upon the character of his early interaction with his mother or mother-substitute.

To telescope much into a few words, as the child matures and the socialization process continues, with its frustrations as well as its satisfactions, the child becomes more and more firmly bound to the socializing agent, more and more dependent rather than more free, and this social binding continues throughout life. This view of the development of the person cannot be too strongly emphasized. Its implications are of the first order of importance. The conventional view of the person in the socializing process as developing to greater and greater individuality is a seriously misleading one. Of course, everyone has a unique personality in the sense that it is never identical with that of any other person, and the differences between personalities are important and tend to become more distinct with age. This is something to be thankful for. But it must be realized that every one of these differences has developed under the influence of socializing factors, and that were it not for the creative action of those socializing factors, the functional-structural differences which characterize each person, would not be as great as they are. Every person is socially bound to the group in which he has been socialized. In this sense the "individual" is a myth. From the standpoint of the social situation there are no individuals, except as abstracted biological entities or for the quantitative purposes of a census. Even from the physical and physiological standpoints, it is doubtful whether the individual has a separate existence in any but an arbitrary sense. Are we not, in the term "individual," creating separateness where separateness does not, in fact, exist? Certainly individualization in man exceeds that attained by any other animal, but it is an individualization which takes place more fully in relation to the group than it does in any other living creature. A creature apart from a social group is nothing but an organic being. The member of a social group is a person, a personality developed under the molding influence of social interstimulation. The person is a set of social relationships. As Bogardus has put it, "As a result of intersocial stimulation, he moves up from the biological level. The interstimulation that occurs between him and members of the group, not as

73

mere individuals but as persons, explains him more than any other method of approach can do." [30]

The "rugged American individualist," for example, is no more an individualist than is a soldier sniping at the enemy. Both behave as they do because they have been subordinated to imperatives which in each case are functions of their social conditioning. They act as they do because they are the results of certain historically conditioned social processes. They act as they do not because they are independent individuals, but because they are dependent persons bound to their social group and must maintain their relationships in that group in the manner, in each case, allowed and encouraged by the group.

Free will the person certainly does not have. The will that he has operates strictly within the limits determined by the pattern of the social group. What he has is the *illusion* of free will. The "spontaneous" conduct of the person is still conduct based on models established in a particular social group. In short, the person is an interdependent system of social relationships which may by abstraction alone be recognized as a unit. As Leo Loeb has recently remarked in a masterly work, "In consequence of the more and more intricate interaction between environment and psychical-social individuality, a separation between individuality and environment, espe-

---

[30] Emory S. Bogardus (Discussion), in Floyd H. Allport, "The Group Fallacy in Relation to Social Science," *American Journal of Sociology*, vol. 29, 1924, p. 704.

cially the social environment, becomes impossible." [31]

And that is the truth which should forever shatter what we must insist on calling the pathetic fallacy, the organismal fallacy that man is essentially a function of his genes. The biologically exclusive sacredness of the individual is a chimera not only as regards man but as regards all other animal groups. The biologist of an earlier day may have cried "the individual for itself." To this the greatest of living physiologists, Sir Charles Sherrington, has made the proper reply:

> The individual? What are the most successful individuals which Life has to show? The multi-cellular. And what has gone to their making? The multi-cellular organism is in itself a variant from the perennial antagonism of cell and cell. Instead of that eternal antagonism, it is a making use of relatedness to bind cell to cell for co-operation. The multi-cellular organism stood for a change, in so far, from conflict between cell and cell to harmony between cell and cell. Its coming was, we know now, pregnant with an immense advance for the whole future of life upon the globe. It was potential of the present success of living forms upon the planet. Implicit in it was for one thing, the emergence of recognizable mind. It was among the many-celled organisms that recognizable mind first appeared. It is surely more than mere analogy to liken to those small beginnings of multi-cellular life of millions of years ago the slender beginnings of altruism today. Evolution has constantly dealt with the relation between physical and mental as

[31] Leo Loeb, *The Biological Basis of Individuality*, Thomas, Springfield, Illinois, 1944, pp. 651-652.

more than mere analogy. The bond of cohesion now arising instead of being as then one of material contact and interchange between related cell-lives is in its nature mental. It is a projection of the self by sympathy with other life into organismal situations besides its immediate own. It is altruism as passion. It marks, we think, at the present time the climax of mind.[32]

To bind cell to cell for co-operation, that is the essence of social life. But no cell is more intricately bound to another than is man to his fellows and his social group. The binding of the individual to his group represents, in fact, a loss of *individual* freedom and a gain in *personal* development through more or less complete identification with the social group. An identification in which the wholeness of the person is preserved only because it is a functioning part of a greater whole—society.

In this process the consciousness of self may actually increase, the sense of personal identity may become even more vivid, and one's ties to one's society more firmly established than ever. Individuation, as the development of personal identity, is neither the contrary nor the contradictory of social identification, it *is* social identification.

The individual—the set of physical and physiological functions—becomes a person with a definite identity only through the process of socialization—the process of becoming identified with a social group. Dissociations such as are implied in the phrases "the self in conflict with society," "man against society," imply a false separation of

[32] Charles Sherrington, *Man on His Nature*, Cambridge University Press, New York, 1941, pp. 387-388.

conditions. Society is made up of interacting selves, of men. It *is* men in interaction. The conditions of conflict which arise in man do not normally originate from within him, from his organic states, but from those social conditions which have a disordering effect upon him and which fail to satisfy his needs. In this sense a neurosis may be produced as the result of a disorder of some part of his social experience to which the person has been unable to adjust himself.

The importance of institutions in determining the nature of neuroses is most clearly seen in those cases in which the structure of the culture is such as to omit any institutionalization of certain forms of behavior. Here, neuroses of certain kinds never occur, whereas in cultures presenting such institutionalized forms of behavior, neurotic forms of behavior with specific reference to these institutions do occur. For example, shamanism and possession are forms of behavior which occur wherever beliefs in the supernatural and the ability of supernatural powers to take possession of certain persons are strongly held. Where such beliefs do not exist or are weakly developed, shamanism does not occur. In medieval Europe, when such beliefs were the rule, witchcraft and possession were common phenomena. With the decline in the belief in the supernatural, witches and possession have all but disappeared in Europe—to be replaced by a counterpart which fits more satisfactorily into the existing cultural structure: the witchcraft and neurosis of modern times known as racism.

Persons, that is socialized individuals, come into being

77

only through social interactions. "They are differentiations within the social field of relations. The group, therefore, is genetically prior to personality." [33]

In short, the physiological dependency of the foetus and the newborn becomes, in society, a socially organized dependency, a social dependency in which the interacting person finds the meaning of his life in his relations with other persons and their thoughts and activities. Unheeded, the physiologically dependent infant would die. Unheeded, the socially dependent adult falls into an apathy which may lead to death. As Erich Fromm has put it, "Unless the person feels that he belongs somewhere, unless his life has some meaning and direction, he would feel like a particle of dust and be overcome by his individual insignificance. He would not be able to relate himself to any system which would give meaning and direction to his life, he would be filled with doubt and this doubt eventually would paralyze his ability to act—that is, to live." [34]

Now, as John Fiske had originally pointed out, and many others since, the long period of dependency which is characteristic of the human infant generates social conditions leading to the peculiar developments of human culture. The importance of this lengthy period of dependence cannot be overemphasized, but the emphasis

[33] John E. Boodin, *The Social Mind*, Macmillan, New York, 1939, p. 155.
[34] Erich Fromm, *Escape from Freedom*, Farrar & Rinehart, New York, 1941, pp. 21-22.

can be and often has been, wrongly placed.[35] Were the anthropoid apes characterized by a period of dependent infancy ten times as long as man's, they would still not develop anything resembling human culture, since they do not possess the necessary neuropsychic potentialities. Failing these, the length of the infant dependency period has a very limited significance for the development of culture, but once granted such potentialities, what we know as peculiarly human society is inevitable.

This is not to say that were the human infant so constructed as to be able to learn to walk, think, talk, and care for himself within a few weeks after birth, human culture would not have developed. It would most certainly have done so, and it is equally certain that the human personality would be an appreciably different thing from what it is today. It is also very likely that societies would be very much more atomistically constructed than they are today. However this may be, the fact is that the prolonged period of infant dependency produces interactive behavior of a kind which within the first six years of the child's life determines the primary pattern of his subsequent social development.

As we have pointed out, it is within this period that he learns to love others: the mother who has so consistently, intimately, and lovingly attended to his needs, the father, his brothers and sisters, and whoever else has participated in the process of satisfying his needs. Certain persons be-

[35] For a recent example, see Geza Roheim's interesting work, *The Origin and Function of Culture*, Nervous and Mental Disease Monographs, New York, No. 69, 1943.

come to him the symbols of satisfaction, for they are always the objects which provide him with the means of satisfaction, and the first conditioning which the child undergoes is this: that persons who have fairly consistently provided the infant with the means of satisfying its needs now become satisfying objects in themselves. The satisfaction of its basic needs become indissolubly associated in the infant's mind with persons who have provided those satisfactions.

The mother is, of course, normally the principal producer of satisfactions and she becomes the first love-object of the child. In this sequence of events, from prenatal to postnatal life, can be seen the determinants, as it were, in high relief, of the pattern of life which every person everywhere seeks to secure, namely, a state of dependency in which one's needs are satisfied by persons whom one (therefore) loves.

What human beings desire most of all is to have their needs satisfied, to be made secure. They also want to feel dependent, either upon some mother-ideal, deity, or other persons, or, pathologically, narcistically upon themselves, but dependent they must feel. Man does not want to be independent, free, in the sense of functioning independently of the interests of his fellows. This kind of negative independence leads to lonesomeness, isolation, and fear. What man wants is that positive freedom which follows the pattern of his life as an infant within the family—dependent security, the feeling that one is a part of a group, accepted, wanted, loved and loving.

The directiveness and creativeness of the human organism at birth is toward realization in terms of dependency upon other organisms. Everything we know points to this fact.

John Donne beautifully expressed these ideas in his seventeenth "Devotion":

> No man is an *Island*, entire of itself; every man is a piece of the *Continent*, a part of the *main*; if a *Clod* be washed away by the *Sea*, *Europe* is the less, as well as if a *Promontory* were, as well as if a *Manor* of thy *friends* or of thine *own* were; any man's *death* diminishes *me*, because I am involved in *Mankind*; And therefore never send to know for whom the *bell* tolls; it tolls for thee.

The phenomenon of transference as seen in the psychoanalytic situation, constitutes, as Freud has pointed out, a proof that adults do not overcome their childhood dependency.[36] In the transference situation, the patient develops relations toward the physician which are clearly derived from emotions originally directed toward the parents. The feelings of dependency upon the parents are transferred to the physician. The patient becomes deeply attached to his analyst, he falls in love with him, overestimates his qualities, will not hear a word said against him, and does everything in his power to maintain the dependent relationship. What he is doing, in effect, is to reproduce the dependency situation of his early infancy. The transference relationship is utilized by the physician to make this clear to the patient and is thus converted into an instrument for his re-education.

[36] Sigmund Freud, "Psychoanalysis," *Encyclopaedia Britannica*, 14th Edition, 1929, pp. 672-674.

A person is not an object in itself, except for census purposes, but a function of activities which he exhibits in interaction with other persons, that is to say, the constituent interacting element of culture. As Harry Stack Sullivan has suggested, personality "is the hypothetical entity that one postulates to account for the doings of people, one with another, and with more or less personified objects." [37] Personality is, in fact, an abstraction, the segmentation of a process at a particular time involving the behavior of a person in relation to others. Whether it is the ego that is doing the segmenting or judging, or other persons, the personality is always a function of relations with other persons. The person is a set of interpersonal relationships, and it is during infancy that the pattern which these shall take is largely determined.

Love is an active state which is learned by the infant, and it is a state which is developed in dependency, and that is the pattern of love which is maintained throughout the life of the person. We love only those things upon which we are dependent—not, however, all things upon which we are dependent: those which are associated with frustration we hate, but those which are associated with pleasure, either present, recollected or anticipated, we love.

Man is related to himself only in so far as he is related to others. To love is to relate oneself to others. The infant is born with drives whose urgency is directed to-

37 Harry S. Sullivan, "Psychiatry: Introduction to the Study of Interpersonal Relations," *Psychiatry*, vol. 1, 1938, pp. 121-134.

ward relating himself to others and to have others relate themselves to him. Life is social and man is born to be social, that is, co-operative, an interdependent part of a whole, a working, interacting part of a community. Again I should like to quote Alfred Adler's mature judgment here:

The individual's proper development can only progress if he lives and strives as a part of the whole. The shallow objections of individualistic systems have no meaning as against this view. I could go still further and show how all our functions are calculated to bind the single individual to the community, and not to destroy the fellowship of man with man. The act of seeing means to receive and make fruitful all that falls on the retina. This is not simply a physiological process; it shows that man is a part of a whole that gives and takes. In seeing, hearing, and speaking, we bind ourselves to one another. Man only sees, hears, and speaks rightly when he is linked to others by his interest in the external world. His reason, his common sense, forms the basis of his control of co-operation, of absolute truth, and aims at eternal rightness. Our aesthetic sense and views—perhaps the strongest powers that impel to great achievements—have an eternal value only when they lead to the well-being of humanity in the direction of the evolutionary stream. All our bodily and mental functions are rightly, normally, and healthily developed insofar as they are imbued with sufficient social feeling and are fitted for co-operation.

When we speak of virtue, we mean that a person plays his part; when we speak of vice, we mean that he interferes with co-operation. I can, moreover, point out that all that constitutes a failure is so because it obstructs social feeling, whether children, neurotics, criminals, or suicides are in question. In every case it can be seen that a contribution is lacking. No isolated persons are to be found in the whole history of humanity. The evolution of humanity was only possible because mankind was a community.

And again:

If the person understood how in evading the demands of evolution, he had gone astray, then he would give up his present course and join the general mass of humanity.

All the problems of human life demand capacity for co-operation and preparation for it—the visible signs of social feeling. In this disposition courage and happiness are included, and they are to be found nowhere else.[38]

[38] A. Adler, *Social Interest: A Challenge to Mankind*, Putnam's, New York, 1938, pp. 282-283 and 284.

# "I" versus "You"

As galt has pointed out, the fundamental unit of social motivation and behavior is not the person but the group. The person no more represents the unit of social behavior than the discrete reflex represents the unit of physiological behavior.[39]

The infant is not born with an ego. It acquires its self from other selves long before it is aware of its own self. Is not this an interesting fact? Its ego, its self, develops only as the infant comes to recognize and adjust to reality. It is clearly not egocentric to begin with. What is usually confused with egocentricity are the generalized dependency needs of the infant which require satisfaction. But such satisfaction is not the demand of an organized ego, for the infant has no ego. The evidence, on the other hand, suggests that it is conditioned to become egocentric by processes of culturalization which emphasize egocentricity. In the cultures of the Western world particularly, the process of socialization while binding the

[39] W. Galt, "The Principle of Cooperation in Behavior," *Quarterly Review of Biology*, vol. 15, 1940, pp. 401-410.

person to his group, has actually the effect of rendering the person functionally asocial. The child is trained in what is expected of him and what he may expect of others. But this training, as Galt points out—

> . . . is subsequent and parallel to a process in which there is a weaning of the child from the sense of biological continuity and solidarity with his kind, and the establishment within him of a sense of personal identity, motivation and authority which of its nature must be in conflict with the identity and motivation of others of his social group. Expressed differently, the total social behavioral pattern which is the biological heritage of the human infant, as it is of other animal species, is disrupted, and an undue individuation takes place. This individuation, which in the course of time sets up an autonomous individual with private hopes, desires, wishes, gains and losses, of necessity brings about severe conflict when the desires of two or more elements or individuals happen to interfere with one another. The incentives to behavior have inadvertently become tied up with the individual as an arbitrary centre of action and motivation rather than with the social group as such a center.[40]

The workers at the Lifwynn Foundation, under the leadership of Trigant Burrow, have found after many years of investigating and analyzing the so-called normal behavior of men in so-called normal communities, that "The normal individual, like the neurotic, [is] . . . constantly thinking and acting in terms of his individual-

[40] *Ibid.*, p. 405.

ized self. He has established an image of himself as
an isolated unit of behavior with private values, wishes
and motivations, and this image dominates his social interrelations." [41] As Burrow says:

> In a word, the individual neurosis is but an exaggeration
> of "normality." It is but an expression, in miniature, of
> the social neurosis. Man is suffering from an organismic
> dislocation from the environment, from an "I"-complex
> or "I"-persona. The partitive sovereignty of the separate
> self. The result is a divisiveness of function, in which
> dissociation and conflict assume supremacy over the
> organism's unity and centralization of function. Man's
> relation to man becomes disordered through the sub-
> ordination of the human organism to the conditioned
> artificial affects and prejudices of the "I"-persona. This
> social mood is divisive to its core, inciting each person
> to compete with others in the interest of the self. The
> principle upon which this divisive socially conditioned
> mood operates is I-versus-you.[42]

In such persons the central principle of creative motivation, the drive to realize the social feeling that is
within them, becomes, if not blocked, then seriously disordered. The personality develops divisively and may become seriously fragmented. At any rate, it largely loses
its power to co-ordinate, to unify, and to operate as a
whole. In Adler's words: "It is always the want of social
feeling, whatever be the name one gives it—living in fel-

[41] *Ibid.*, p. 407.
[42] Burrow, "The Social Neurosis: A Study in 'Clinical Anthropology,'"
*Philosophy of Science*, vol. 16, 194, pp. 25-40.

lowship, co-operation, humanity, or even the ideal-ego
—which causes an insufficient preparation for all the
problems of life. In the presence of a problem, this im-
perfect preparation gives rise to the thousand-fold forms
that express physical and mental inferiority and insecurity." [43]

The suppressed voices of our inner consciousness tell
us what we ought to be, of the life we have not lived, but
could have lived had not something, we know not quite
what, happened to determine otherwise. That "something" is the conditioning process to which we were exposed as infants and children. It is that which has made
us, in the Western world, the partitive, disordered, hostile, egocentric creatures we have become. We are out
of line with our evolutionary destiny, which is integration and co-operation, *not* disintegration and disopera-
tion. On the personal, the community, national, and
international planes, the effects are the same of an "I"-
persona conditioning, namely, disorder, disease, and dis-
operation. To quote Burrow once more:

> It is useless to essay a policy of social and economic co-
> operation on a non-cooperative basis of motivation. We
> will achieve a pattern of social cooperation and harmony
> among individuals and nations only when we have ac-
> cepted the pattern on internal balance and coordination
> within the organism of man as a species. As things stand
> today, in this world of division and conflict, the war we

[43] A. Adler, *Social Interest: A Challenge to Mankind,* Putnam's, New
York, 1938, p. 110.

have fought will have been fought in vain. It will have been no less vain than the many political and economic wars that have preceded it. Vain too must be the unilateral program of peace that will issue out of it. All our international covenants, all our external diplomatic treaties, all the peace programs yet to be devised must remain forever unavailing if our behavior dichotomies and antagonisms are ultimately traceable to a functional brain-twist that is internal to the organism of man as a race.[44]

The functional brain-twist is the "I"-persona conditioning of the frontal lobes which opposes itself to man's innate drives toward its contradictory, co-operation.
This writer agrees with Adler that

A careful consideration of individual and collective existence, both past and present, shows us the struggle of mankind for a stronger social feeling. One can scarcely fail to see that humanity is conscious of this problem and is impressed by it. Our present-day burdens are the result of the lack of a thorough social education. It is the pent-up social feeling in us that urges us to reach a higher stage and to rid ourselves of the errors that mark our public life and our own personality. This social feeling exists within us and endeavors to carry out its purpose; it does not seem strong enough to hold its own against all opposing forces. The justified expectation persists that in a far-off age, if mankind is given enough time, the power of social feeling will triumph over all that opposes it. Then it will be as natural to man as

[44] T. Burrow, *Op. cit.*

breathing. For the present the only alternative is to understand and to teach that this will inevitably happen.[45]

One point upon which one might disagree with Adler is the last. It is perhaps dangerous to suggest that social feeling will inevitably triumph. On the other hand, if we go on as we have been doing, the chances are fairly high that we will exterminate ourselves. What is necessary is to understand and to teach the implications of the facts as we have come to know them, and what it is that needs to be done.

Furthermore, a point which Adler overlooked, is that the harmonic, co-operative life in which social feeling does appear to be almost as natural as breathing has been achieved by several human groups—groups whom we used to call "savage," then "primitive," and now, thanks to the intervention of the anthropologist, "nonliterate peoples." The best known examples of such groups are to be found among the Australian aborigines and the Eskimos.

The Australian aborigines know neither the domestication of animals nor agriculture. They are food-gatherers and hunters and are generally regarded as among the most primitive of living peoples; indeed, they are a Stone Age people. Yet this nonliterate Stone Age people (actually there are many different tribes, but the following statements hold true for all of them) lives in peace and

45 A. Adler, *Social Interest: A Challenge to Mankind*, Putnam's, New York, 1938, p. 285.

harmony with its fellows, is quite unacquainted with war, and never does anything from the profit-motive. On the contrary, the socialization process takes such a form that the child grows up to be a happy, joyous, secure person, who rarely, if ever, does anything but that he thinks of the consequences of his acts for his fellows.

Similarly, all who have known the Eskimos of the Arctic and Alaska have been impressed by their complete co-operation and sense of personal responsibility to their fellows. Numerous books, from Stefansson, through Peter Freuchen to Gontran de Poncins, have been written about the Eskimos and their way of life. Many a sophisticated, and many a simple, white man has fallen under their spell and settled among them. Missionaries who have gone out to save the souls of the aborigines of Australia and the aborigines of the Far North, have been known to say that it was not the souls of the aborigines which needed saving but those of the white men among them.

There are many other nonliterate, and some literate, peoples who exhibit a highly developed and sensitive awareness of their co-operative relation to their fellow men.

Foreigners who have dwelt among these peoples have frequently commented on the delightful breeding of the children and their sunny personalities. Anthropologists are beginning to discover that this is indeed a fact and that it is largely the result of the permissiveness and low frequency of frustration to which these children are exposed. Such children tend to grow into secure, well-integrated adult personalities. The institutions of these societies, the social arrangements, that is to say, for maintaining the structure of the society, serve to maintain the security of the personality by the assurance which they afford it in terms of nonfrustrative, co-operative support.

In a book as short as this it is not possible to treat of these cultures at any length. The interested reader may, however, read further on this subject in the works listed below.[46]

The view that the child is born egocentric, evil, in "sin," is widely held, and it is nothing more than a projection upon the child of our own conditioning in egocentricity, in evil, in "sin." Such a view is not supported by the facts. The facts, on the contrary, show that the child is born as an actively co-operating organism. Charlotte Bühler has pointed out that co-operative behavior among children is more basic than competitive response, finding that the latter type of response in her group of observed children did not make its appearance till about the third year.[47]

[46] S. S. Sargent and M. W. Smith (editors), *Culture and Personality*, The Viking Fund, New York, 1949; D. G. Haring, *Personal Character and Cultural Milieu*, Syracuse University Press, 1949.

[47] C. Bühler, *"Die Ersten Sozialen Verhaltungsweisen des Kindes," Soziologische und Psychologische Studien über das Erste Legensjahr*, Fischer, Jena, 1927; C. Bühler, "Spontaneous Reactions of Children in the First Two Years," *Proceedings and Papers of the 9th International Congress of Psychology*, 1929, pp. 99-100.

All observers have found that hostile responses in the child tend to increase as it grows older.[48]

From her vast experience, Bender finds that, far from being inborn, hostility in the child "is a symptom complex resulting from deprivations which are caused by developmental discrepancies in the total personality structure such that the constructive patterned drives for action in the child find inadequate means of satisfaction and result in amplification or disorganization of the drives into hostile or destructive aggression." "The child," she writes, "acts as though there were an inherent awareness of his needs and there is thus the expectation of having them met. A failure in this regard is a deprivation and leads to frustration and a reactive aggressive response." [49]

Indeed, the creativeness of the organism is directed toward maturation in terms of co-operation. Bender calls it "the inherent capacity or drive for normality." And she says, "The emphasis on the inborn or instinctive features of hostility, aggression, death wishes, and the negative emotional experiences represents a onesided approach which has led our students of child psychology astray."

The infant soon learns that in order to be satisfied, in order to be loved, he too must satisfy, he too must love, he must satisfy the requirements of others, he must co-

[48] M. J. Muste and D. F. Sharpe, "Some Influential Factors in the Determination of Aggressive Behavior in Pre-school Children," *Child Development,* vol. 18, 1947, pp. 11-28.
[49] L. Bender, "Genesis of Hostility in Children," *American Journal of Psychiatry,* vol. 105, 1948, pp. 241-245.

operate, he must actually give up or postpone the satisfaction of certain desires if he is to achieve satisfaction in others and if he is to retain the love of those whose love he needs. This, too, is a recognizable adult pattern of behavior which takes its origin in early experiences. From the beginning, this pattern of behavior provides the most fundamentally important means by which the socialization of the organism is achieved. First, through love as a feeling of belongingness (security), and second, through love as authority, the authority of the affectionate tie. "I belong to this family, and it is because these people love me that I belong. I like to belong, therefore I must obey them and retain their love so that I may continue to belong." This is what the child resolves for himself though he may never give conscious expression to the thought. The relationships within his family condition the personal relationships throughout his life. "They are loaded with affection and carry the burden of giving to each a *place*—a sense of belonging, a meaning to the process of arriving and being." [50]

Outside the family, as a "grown-up," he secures the approval (love) of his fellows by conforming to the standards of the group. This is the family pattern repeated on a less intensive more extensive scale. To conform means the willingness to forego certain satisfactions in order to obtain others, to suffer a certain amount of deprivation and thwarting of satisfactions as a discipline

[50] James Plant, *Personality and the Cultural Pattern*, The Commonwealth Fund, New York, 1937, p. 267.

94

which may ultimately lead to what are socially esteemed as greater rewards. A certain degree of conflict, repression, and aggressiveness are the consequences of such experiences both in the family and in the group in all cultures.

# Fission versus Fusion

As WE HAVE POINTED OUT, THE FAILURE TO DEVELOP social competence is due to the privation of love suffered by the infant during the first six years of life. We are thus led to conclude that in order to be successfully social, one must have learned to love by having been loved; that, indeed, society is based on love, in fact *is* but a developed form of love. That where hatreds exist in any persons within any society we may be sure that they, too, are due to love, for hatred is love frustrated. Aggression is but a technique or mode of seeking love.

Love is in its essence, in its beginning and end, social. It arises out of the satisfaction of the self-preservative or basic needs of the organism in the primary dependent relationship to the parent, and it demands always the presence of other persons or their substitutes in order to function adequately.

Man's need for society and his need for love are one and the same thing. Ian Suttie, in a brilliant book, has suggested that "play, co-operation, competition and culture-interests generally are substitutes for the mutually

caressing relationship of child and mother. *By these sub-*
*stitutes we put the whole social environment in the place*
*once occupied by the mother."* [51]

The organism is born with an innate need for love,
with a need to respond to love, to be good, co-operative.
This is, I believe, now established beyond any shadow of
doubt. Whatever is opposed to love, to goodness, and to
co-operation is disharmonic, unviable, unstable, and mal-
functional—evil. Were the infant's needs adequately satisfied, he could not help being good—that is, loving. All
of man's natural inclinations are toward the development
of goodness, toward the continuance of states of goodness and the discontinuance of unpleasant states. As
Ralph Lillie has pointed out:

> . . . a property of the good (in the universal or Pla-
> tonic sense) is that unconscious effort is inevitably di-
> rected toward its continuance (since it is the object of
> desire) while evil, the immediately or ultimately pain-
> ful, is a feature of reality which conscious effort tends
> to remove or overcome. The former has thus within
> itself a property or character which favors its continu-
> ance; the latter is inherently unstable. Analysis shows
> that stability in all highly diversified or composite sys-
> tems requires harmonious relations (relations of balance
> or equilibrium) between the different components and
> activities . . . modern biology recognizes that integra-
> tion between different types of individual as seen in the
> cooperative relations between units in human and ani-

[51] Ian D. Suttie, *The Origins of Love and Hate*, Kegan Paul, London,
1935, p. 16.

mal communities (or even between different species of animals or plants), is as much of a factor in survival and evolution as is conflict. The avoidance of useful conflict, and the subordination of individual interests to the interest of the integrated whole which includes the individuals, would thus seem to be rational aims for conscious beings; and these aims have the further sanction of religion when the whole is conceived in its character as ultimate value or deity.[52]

The biological basis of love consists in the organism's drive to satisfy its basic needs in a manner which causes it to feel secure. Love *is* security. Mere satisfaction of basic needs is not enough. Needs must be satisfied in a particular manner, in a manner which is emotionally as well as physically satisfying.

To repeat, the biological basis of love lies in the organism's ever-present urge to feel secure, and it would appear that the basis of all social life has its roots in this integral of all the basic needs which is expressed as the need for security, and that the only way in which this need can be satisfied is by love.

It is a discovery of the greatest possible significance for mankind that the ethical conception of love independently arrived at by almost all existing peoples is no mere creation of man but is grounded in the biological structure of man as a functioning organism. The implications of this discovery are of the very greatest importance, for it means that man's organic potentialities are

[52] Ralph S. Lillie, "The Psychic Factor in Living Organisms," *Philosophy of Science*, vol. 10, 1943, pp. 262-270.

so organized as to demand but one kind of satisfaction alone, a satisfaction which ministers to man's need for love, which registers love, which is given in terms of love—a satisfaction which is defined by the one word, *security*. That is what the human being seeks all his life, and society, culture, and man's institutions, however inefficient some of them may be, all exist to secure that one fundamental satisfaction. The emotional need for love is as definite and compelling as the need for food. The basic needs of man must be satisfied in order that he may function on the organic level. But in order that he may function satisfactorily on the social plane, the most fundamental of the basic social needs must be satisfied in an emotionally adequate manner for personal security or equilibrium.

It has been shown that when the needs of the developing social organism are inadequately satisfied, that is, where there have been too many frustrations—thwartings of expected satisfactions—where there has been a privation of love, the organism becomes disordered, anxious, tense, fearful, and hostile. This, in fact, is more or less the state into which most human beings in the Western world today have fallen.

In the preceding pages it has been suggested that the biological basis of co-operation has its origins in the same sources as social behavior, namely, in the process of reproduction. It has been shown that social, co-operative behavior is simply the continuation and development of the parent-offspring relationship. Co-operative, social behavior is therefore as old as life itself, and the direction of evolution has, in man, been increasingly directed toward the fuller development of co-operative behavior.

Co-operative behavior clearly has great survival value. When social behavior is not co-operative, it is diseased. The dominant principle which informs all behavior that is biologically healthy is love. Without love there can be no healthy social behavior, co-operation, or security. To love thy neighbor as thyself is not simply good text material for Sunday morning sermons but perfectly sound biology.

Men who do not love one another are sick—sick not from any disease arising within themselves but from a disease which has been enculturated within them by the false values of their societies. Belief in false values which condition the development of the person, in competition instead of co-operation, in narrow selfish interests instead of altruism, in atomism (especially atom-bombism and at this writing, hydrogen-bombism) instead of universalism, in the value of money instead of the value of man, represents man turning upon all that is innately good in him.

Thus, in our society, there are conflicting and mutually irreconcilable institutions which put too great a strain upon the adaptive capacities of most persons. The Christian ethic of love in relation to the business ethic of competition or "free enterprise," for example. On the one hand, we expose our children to a system of ideal teachings which we call Christianity, and which we more or less endeavor to instill into them, while, on the other hand, we increasingly expose them to precepts and examples which place a high value upon competition. We pay lip service to spiritual values but place our faith in material possessions. Our prices and our values have become sadly confused. Is laissez-faire capitalism, free enterprise, compatible with Christianity, with co-operation, with love? The individual may never explicitly ask himself such questions, but there is not the least doubt that they create dilemmas within him which he is never able to solve, and which substantially contribute to rendering him the problem, the unsolved problem he becomes.

Man's sense of mutuality and co-operativeness may be suppressed, but so long as man continues to exist, it cannot be destroyed, for these are traits which are part of his protoplasm. His combativeness and competitiveness arise primarily from the frustration of his need to co-operate. These are important facts to bear in mind at a time when all the surface evidence seems to point in a contrary direction. The word of the moment may be "fission"—whether with respect to physics or human affairs—but "fusion" comes much closer to reflecting man's natural behavior patterns.

Science points the way to survival and happiness for all mankind through love and co-operation. Do what we will, our drives toward goodness are as biologically determined as are our drives toward breathing. Our highly endowed potentialities for social life have been used to pervert and deny their very nature, and this has led us close to the brink of disaster, a disaster which spells doom unless we realize what we have done and take the proper steps to undo it before it is too late. For we cannot, without destroying ourselves, deny the power of the world forces which we share with all life and which have reached their highest development in our potentialities as human beings.

Our world at the present time is largely directed by criminally irresponsible adventurers and cynical and complacent men who have grown old in the ways of self-interest and ultranationalism. Unless their place is taken by men of understanding and humility, whose guiding principle is love, the world of man is doomed.

The life of every human being is a part of our own, for we are involved in mankind. Each one of us is responsible for the other. It was Dostoevski who said, "Each of us is responsible for everything to everyone else." That is what we now know. It is up to us to do something with that knowledge.

# 3

# The Improvement of Human Relations through Education

# The Fourth *R*

---

*W*HAT CAN BE DONE SHOULD BE SUFFICIENTLY CLEAR
from the preceding pages. What man needs is a change
in attitudes of mind. His attitudes must be based on the
principle of co-operation, the principle of love, for it is
then that he operates most efficiently in terms of genu-
ine human happiness. This is really not easier said than
done. All human beings want to be good. All human
beings want to be happy. Their biological drives are calculated to achieve those ends. But most human beings
in our culture are confused about means and ends in doing good and in securing happiness. Evil means are often
used to secure "good" ends, and so-called "good" means
are sometimes used to secure evil ends. If man can but
be persuaded to try living in co-operation with his fellow
men, he will discover that it is no more difficult to do so
than to say so. For the drives toward co-operation are
all there within him, and they are his *dominant* drives.
Man has but to give them the opportunity to express
themselves.

The wonderful thing about the principle of co-operation is that in addition to proving the value of co-operation as a way of life, it also proves that co-operation, love, is *a means which when applied to human relations is the most conducive of all to the establishment of good human relations.*

It is the belief of this writer that, in addition to what each person can himself do, here and now, the best results will be secured through the long-term agency of education. For this reason the final part of this book will be devoted to a consideration of the improvement of human relations through education.

In our schools we teach the three *r*'s; the fourth *r*, relations, *human relations*, it has been said, we do not teach. I think this is no more true than to say that what is wrong with most people of the Western world today is that they have no values. Unfortunately, the trouble with most of us is not that we have no values but that we have too many of the wrong kind. Similarly, it is not true to say that we fail to teach human relations in our schools. We do teach such relations not only in a negative way but we teach them in an unmistakably positive way. And it is, on the whole, a way which is of the most unfortunate kind.

Organized instruction in human relations, when it is not left to the coach on the football or baseball team, is generally more honored in the breach than in the observance. But unorganized instruction in human relations occurs in all schools. From the principal to the janitor, children learn how to behave in relation to others—not so much from what is said as from what these conscious and unconscious preceptors do. Example is stronger than precept, and imitation is the most immediate form of learning. Words have no meaning other than the action they produce. And in our schools words are activated by what the teachers believe. From every standpoint, then, it is important that teachers, the unacknowledged legislators of the world, shall believe in the right things. For unless they do so, their words and conduct, no matter how noble the sentiments they are supposed to express, will be recognized for the counterfeit coin they are.

There are today, for example, many teachers in our schools who are teaching race prejudice to their pupils. They do this not by means of prepared courses in the subject but by their attitudes—by a look, an expression, an inflection of the voice, or the weighting of a word. Though they have never been formulated in so many words, the views of such teachers on the subject of race and race relations are clearly understood by, and exert a considerable influence upon, their pupils. Such teachers do not belong in a school. The principal function of the teacher is, or should be, to help prepare the child for living a humane and co-operative life, not to infect his mind with the antihuman virus of racism.

No one should ever be permitted to become a teacher of the young unless by temperament, attitudes, and training he is fitted to do so. The teacher is the most important of all the public servants of the community; for what service can be more important to the community than the kind of molding of the mind and channeling of the social behavior of the future citizen which the teacher is able to direct? The anything but princely stipends with which he is rewarded for his services suggest that our society does not recognize the true value or function of the teacher.

The school is a place of instruction. It is not really a place of education in the proper sense of that word—in the sense of bringing out the best in a person. In conformity with the requirements of a burgeoning industrial civilization, techniques and technology are at a premium. What can be used to succeed in such a society becomes that which is most emphasized during the learning period, the rest is sheer luxury. From such a standpoint it is but natural that we should come to believe that the function of the school is essentially to teach the three *r*'s in terms of the crude needs of an industrial civilization.

Clearly, values here are sadly mixed. They are the values of the world's largest industrial civilization. The value "success" in such a civilization is measured in terms of dollars. A man's worth in such a civilization is not his quality but his quantity, quantity of dollars, possessions.

Validation of success in terms of externals has become the mark of our civilization. In such a value system, human relations take on the ethical values of the salesman. The idols of the market-place reign supreme. Competition is the most powerful law. The competitive personality governed by the ideals of an industrial society must always be out in front. He must be better than others, for to be so yields the greatest returns. In the world of a person so conditioned, it is taken for granted that some persons are inferior to others in their capacity to achieve. To most such persons the notion that there are whole groups of mankind which are unimprovably inferior is not only acceptable but indispensably necessary, for it constitutes at once a proof of the validity of the system and an incentive to go ahead and reap its benefits. It is a fully fledged belief in the doctrine of the survival of the fittest. The fit are those who are going to succeed or who have already succeeded, while the unfit are those who are not going to succeed, and it is, of course, most convenient and useful to know beforehand what groups of men are *not* going to succeed.

The very large amount of mental disorder, nervous tension, conflict, fear, anxiety, frustration, and insecurity which occurs in Western society is largely due to the failure of the values in which we have been conditioned since infancy—false values by which we seek to live. The fact is that human beings cannot be false to each other and to themselves without breaking down under the strain, however often they may attempt to relieve themselves of their frustrations and anxieties by attacking their scapegoats.

Man is born for co-operation, not for competition or conflict. This is a basic discovery of modern science. It confirms a discovery made some two thousand years ago by one Jesus of Nazareth. In a word: it is the principle of love which embraces all mankind. It is the principle of humanity, of one world, one brotherhood of peoples.

The measure of a person's humanity is the extent and

intensity of his love for mankind. That measure is not the extent or intensity of his knowledge of the three *r*'s. If mankind is to be saved, it can be done only by replacing the values of industrial technology with those of humanity, of co-operation, of love. It is only when humanity is in control that technology in the service of humanity will occupy its proper place in the scheme of things. A most important and immediate task is to make the people understand this. It is the duty of everyone capable of doing so to undertake this task. There must be a complete revaluation and reorientation of our values.

The school beyond all else must be considered as a place of education in the art and science of being a person, the practice of human relations. Let us recall here the words of Franklin Delano Roosevelt from the 1945 Jefferson Day speech which, so tragically, he did not live to deliver:

> . . . the mere conquest of our enemies is not enough. We must go on to do all in our power to conquer the doubts and the fears, the ignorance and the greed which made this horror possible.
>
> Today, we are faced with the pre-eminent fact that *if civilization is to survive, we must cultivate the science of human relationships—the ability of all peoples, of all kinds, to live together and work together in the same world at peace.*

Without in any way underemphasizing the important influence which the home constitutes, I believe that the school must be considered as a most important agency in the teaching of the art and science of human relations.

We must shift the emphasis from the three *r*'s to the fourth *r*, human relations, and place it first, foremost, and always in that order of importance, as the principal reason for the existence of the school. It must be clearly understood, once and for all time, that human relations are the most important of all relations. Upon this understanding must be based all our educational policies. We must train for humanity, and training in reading, writing, and arithmetic must be given in a manner calculated to serve the ends of that humanity. For all the knowledge in the world is worse than useless if it is not humanely understood and humanely used. An intelligence that is not humane is the most dangerous thing in the world.

Our teachers must, therefore, be specially qualified to teach human relations. The importance of their function must be recognized and suitably rewarded by a society anxious to encourage the entry of the best kind of people into the professional privilege of preparing human beings for the art of living. There can be no more important task than this. It is a task which demands qualities of the highest order. The teacher must be temperamentally fitted for his profession, and he should himself be an exemplar of the art of living and the practice of human relations. Children would learn more from such a teacher than from all the factually informed instructors in the world.

Are these specifications visionary? Certainly they will not be achieved if we think so. It is this writer's belief not only that they can be achieved, but that it is our moral duty to see that they are brought into existence. Pallia-

tive piece-meal approaches are not enough. If we are to
cure the disease, we must attack its causes.

Prominent among these causes are the substitution of
economics for humanity, the substitution of competition
for co-operation, frustration of our children for the permissiveness which should be their right, the piling up
of unexpanded aggressiveness within them, and the production of conflicts and insecurities incident to the structure of a competitive society—a society which, on the one
hand, preaches brotherly love and, on the other, practices
self-love and the denial of brotherhood.

Most human beings want to like, to love, their fellow
men. Yet in their everyday lives they, for the most part,
practice self-love and are more or less hostile toward all
those whom they conceive to stand in their way. The
reason for this tragic disparity between what they feel
to be right and what they do is simply that the structure
of this society is such that the life of the person becomes
reduced to a competitive struggle for existence. Under
such conditions, men everywhere become nasty, brutish,
and cruel. They become atomistic, selfish, individualistic.
Under such a system it is hard for them to do otherwise,
for the first law of life is and has always been self-preser-
vation (the satisfaction of basic needs), and if the individual will not do everything in his power to gain security for himself, who will? Well might he echo that
Talmudic voice which said: "If I am not for myself,
who will be for me? If I am for myself only, what am I?
If not now—when?"

In such a society man lives for himself alone; he is

forced to. The right of other persons to existence is acknowledged in so far as it contributes to his security. Those persons or groups who may be conceived as constituting an obstacle to that achievement therefore evoke hostile and aggressive responses. Yet these same persons know from such religious training as they may have had that this conduct is wrong and evil.

Were the conditions provided for such persons to lead the good life in harmony with all men, can there be the least doubt that they would take full advantage of those conditions?

In order to live the good life, it is first necessary to live. If the structure of society is such that it makes of life a struggle for bare physical existence, in which frustration and insecurity are maximized, in which the person is left to sink or swim entirely alone, there is little time and no incentive to lead the good life. In an industrial civilization with its emphasis on success in terms of material values, success is generally achieved in material terms at the expense of truly human values.

Western society, in short, does not encourage the development of goodness because goodness is not what that society is interested in. Goodness belongs to a frame of reference other than that in which we make our living. It belongs to the covert rather than to the overt part of our culture. What we must do is to enthrone goodness, human relations, in the place at present occupied by economics. The idols of the market place must yield to those of humanity. A society such as ours, in which human relations are submerged in the economic system, can rescue itself only by submerging its economy in the matrix of human relations.

And this is the task that the schools must assist in undertaking, no less than the rescue of man from his debasing enslavement to the principles and practices of an acquisitive society.

Those who would have us believe that almost everything in the world is determined by economics are wrong. Certainly if you build a society on economic foundations and you make the whole superstructure dependent upon those foundations, economic determinism will be a most influentially operative principle. But only in a society which is so structured. If you identify human nature with economics, with production, you make of a man a commodity, and you create a system of material values which readily lends itself to exploitation. When you build your society upon the foundation of human relations, as so many nonliterate societies have done, the processes of getting a living are co-operative; no one does anything for gain, the profit motive is nonexistent, and the individual feels secure in the knowledge that as long as there is anything to eat, every member in the group will eat. The menace of insecurity is collectively eliminated and individual destitution unknown. The determinants of conduct in such a society stem from social organization and religion, from the human relations of the group, as do the determinants of economic behavior.

The motives of human beings everywhere are human, *not* economic. They are made to become economic only in societies in which moneytheism is the prevailing religion. If, then, we would establish a world of humanity, we must educate human motivations in terms of humanity and not of economics. We must remove economics as the dominant motive from human relations and make human relations the dominant motive in economics.

Let no one be deceived. Unless Western man is able to release himself from the degrading tyranny of his enslavement to the religion of economics, he is as certainly doomed to self-destruction as all the portents indicate. Man cannot live by bread alone. Physiologically, biologically, psychologically, and socially, he can retain his health and flourish only in love of, and co-operation with, his fellow man.

A profit-motive, economic-struggle-for-existence society is a predatory society, a class-and-caste society, a divisive society, in which each person is an isolate preying upon and preyed upon by others. Economic security, power, and prestige are the objectives which determine the motivations of men in such a society. Under such conditions men attempt to limit the opportunities for successful achievement to themselves. Few succeed and most are caused to fail. This is the chief result, as well as the cause, of class and caste distinctions. The frustration and aggressiveness so produced is enormous. Professor Robert K. Merton has brilliantly described the frustrative mechanism in our society.

> It is only when a system of cultural values extols, virtually above all else, certain common symbols of success *for the population at large*, while its social structure rigorously restricts or completely eliminates access to

approved modes of acquiring these symbols *for a considerable part of the same population,* that antisocial behavior ensues on a considerable scale. In other words, our egalitarian ideology denies by implication the existence of noncompeting groups and individuals in the pursuit of pecuniary success. The same body of success symbols is held to be desirable for all. These goals are held to *transcend class lines,* not to be bound by them, yet the actual social organization is such that there exist class differentials in the accessibility of these *common* success symbols. Frustration and thwarted aspiration lead to the search for avenues of escape from a culturally induced intolerable situation; or unrelieved ambition may eventuate in illicit attempts to acquire the dominant values. The American stress on pecuniary success and ambitiousness for all thus invites exaggerated anxieties, hostilities, neuroses, and antisocial behavior.[53]

Race prejudice and discrimination are among the consequences of such anarchic conditions, and these racial hostilities will not be removed until these conditions are removed. Hence, let it be clearly understood that teaching of the facts of race in the schools and elsewhere, intercultural programs, Springfield Plans and the like, while they may help as palliatives, will not substantially solve the problem, though they may contribute toward its solution. The problem we have to solve is first and foremost the problem of how we can rebuild our society in terms of human values in which human relations are given a chance to function as they should. No matter what we

[53] Robert K. Merton, "Social Structure and Anomie," *American Sociological Review,* vol. 3, 1938, p. 680.

teach in the schools concerning the equality of man, unless these teachings are provided with a social milieu in which they can be practiced, they will wilt and die in the breasts of those who are forced to adapt themselves to the world as they find it.

How, then, is this problem to be solved?

The answer is: Through social engineering. Who are to be the engineers? The answer to that is: The children who are to be the adult members of the next generations. How are they to be prepared for their task? By being taught as clearly and as soundly as possible what the nature of our society is, why it must be modified, and how it can be changed, and this must constitute part and parcel of their training in human relations. Thus, at once will they be equipped with the reason and the means of bringing about the new dispensation of man.

This must be our program, courageously and unequivocally expressed, for our cause is in the interest of every human being, of all mankind. There can be no nobler cause. It is up to the educators of America not only to be its standard bearers but with the co-operation of the enlightened part of our citizenry to undertake its realization.

There will be opposition and there will be difficulties, but opposition and difficulties exist in order to be surmounted. Nothing was ever achieved without trying. And each of us who is in a position to do so can begin by trying to introduce these ideas in our communities. Tact, discretion, conviction, and above all, courage will be required. On our side we start with some handicaps, the greatest of these being inertia and the fear of failure. But we must remember that we have the greatest of all advantages on our side: the soundness of our cause, and, in addition, the consciousness of modern man that all is not well either with himself or with his world, and his desire for a better life.

Our task is to convince those who need to be convinced of the soundness of our cause and the benefits which will accrue to all men from its adoption. Intelligently planned and properly presented, I have little doubt that it will earn the support of a sufficient number of persons to enable it to get away to a good start.

The problem of human relations is one which can be solved. If we would have happy human relations, we must have a society based on human relations and not on economics. This, therefore, is what we must work to achieve. All else must be considered as subordinate and ancillary to this main task.

We know the problem, we know the solution. Let us then ask ourselves the question: Are we part of the problem or are we part of the solution?

# For
# Further Reading

Benedict, Ruth. *The Chrysanthemum and the Sword.* Houghton Mifflin, Boston, 1946.
A study of Japanese culture and personality.

Davis, Allison W. and Havighurst, Robert J. *Father of the Man.* Houghton Mifflin, 1947.
How the child gets its personality.

Fromm, Erich. *Escape from Freedom.* Farrar & Rinehart, New York, 1941.
A brilliant book on the social development and status of man in the Western world today.

——. *Man for Himself.* Rinehart, New York, 1947.
An inquiry into the psychology of moral development in modern man.

Havighurst, Robert J. and Taba, Hilda. *Adolescent Character and Personality.* Wiley & Sons, New York, 1949.
A report on adolescent youth in a midwestern town.

Hollingshead, A. B. *Elmtown's Youth.* Wiley & Sons, New York, 1949.
The class system and its effect upon the development of personality, as studied in a typical American town.

Leighton, Dorothea and Kluckhohn, Clyde. *Children of the People.* Harvard University Press, Cambridge, 1947.
A study of the Navaho Indian and his development as a person.

Mead, Margaret. *And Keep Your Powder Dry.* Morrow, New York, 1942.
An admirable study of the development of the American character.

Patten, William. *The Grand Strategy of Evolution*. Richard G. Badger, Boston, 1920.
One of the great books on the importance of the principle of co-operation in nature.

Rodnick, David. *Postwar Germans*. Yale University Press, New Haven, 1948.
An account of the postwar German's personality, and how it got to be that way.

Schaffner, Bertram. *Father Land*. Columbia University Press, New York, 1948.
A study of authoritarianism in the German family.

West, James. *Plainville, U.S.A.* Columbia University Press, 1945.
An account of everyday life in a typical rural American town.

Whyte, L. L. *The Next Development in Man*. Henry Holt, New York, 1948.
——. *Everyman Looks Forward*. Henry Holt, 1948.
——. *The Unitary Principle in Physics and Biology*. Henry Holt, 1949.
The first two books by Whyte present a most penetrating and original analysis of man in the world today and the course he needs to pursue for the future. The third book is a fascinating sketch of the belief (to be developed in a larger and more technical work) in the unity of nature and the essential unity of all knowledge.

Yang, Martin C. *A Chinese Village*. Columbia University Press, 1945.
A study of a typical Chinese village and its socialization processes.

# Acknowledgments

Thanks are due to the following publishers for permission to quote from the books published by them:

Appleton-Century Company, R. M. & H. Bakwin, *Psychologic Care During Infancy and Childhood.*

Columbia University Press, Margaret Ribble. *The Rights of Infants.*

Farrar & Rinehart, Erich Fromm, *Escape from Freedom.*

Harcourt, Brace & Company, E. M. Forster, *Abinger Harvest.*

Harcourt, Brace & Company, W. M. Wheeler, *The Social Life of Insects.*

Harper & Brothers, T. H. & J. Huxley, *Touchstone for Ethics.*

The Macmillan Company, John E. Boodin, *The Social Mind.*

The Macmillan Company, Charles Sherrington, *Man on His Nature.*

W. W. Norton, W. C. Allee, *The Social Life of Animals.*

G. P. Putnam's Sons, A. Adler, *Social Interest: A Challenge to Mankind.*

Charles Scribner's Sons, Charles H. Cooley, *The Social Process.*